# Our Little Cuban Cousin

## Mary Hazelton Blanchard Wade

# OUR LITTLE CUBAN COUSIN

## CHAPTER I

### DANGER

"Maria! Maria! Maria!" was the low call from some unknown direction. It sounded like a whisper, yet it must have travelled from a distance. Low as it was, the little girl dozing in the hammock in the lemon grove was awake in an instant. She sprang out and stood with hands shading her eyes, looking for the owner of the voice.

She well knew what it meant. Ramon was the only one who had agreed to call in this way. It was a sign of danger! It meant, "The enemies are coming. Look out and get ready." Shouldn't you think our little Cuban cousin would have trembled and cried, or at least run for protection to her mother?

Maria was only nine years old. She was a perfect fairy of a child, with tiny hands and feet and soft black eyes. But she was used to war by this time. She never knew when she went to sleep at night but that her home would be burnt down by the cruel Spaniards before the end of another day.

Ramon got up before sunrise this morning. He had been away from home for several hours. He had gone out in the country "to look around," as he said. From his own front door the burning roofs of the houses of old friends not a mile distant could be seen the night before. The Spanish troops must be near. Who could say but that the boy's own home would suffer next?

He was tall and active, and he longed very much to help his people. They had suffered much from their Spanish rulers and now they were working hard for freedom. But Ramon's father had been ill for a long time. He was growing weaker every day. The boy's mother looked very sad at times. Her eyes filled with tears when she said:

"My dear boy, you must not leave us now. Your duty lies at home. You must be your father's right hand and protect your little sisters and myself."

The Diaz children lived in a cosy little home in the country. It was only a few miles from Havana. Their father had a small sugar plantation. He had been

2

able to raise enough sugar to buy everything the family needed until lately. But now times were very hard. It was not easy to sell the sugar; besides this, the good man and his family were in constant danger.

What had they done? you ask. Nothing. They did not love their Spanish rulers, to be sure, and they believed their countrymen were fighting justly to free their beautiful island home. They would help these countrymen, or insurgents, as they were called, if they had a chance.

But Maria's father had never, himself, fought against the Spaniards. He was a quiet, kindly gentleman, and he had no love for war. What did the Spaniards care for that? They might say to themselves:

"This man has a pleasant home. He raises sugar. He may give food and shelter to those daring Cuban soldiers. Then they can keep up their strength and be able to keep up the fight against us all the longer."

So far Maria's home had been spared. Although many other houses near her had been burned, hers stood safe and unharmed yet. But "To-morrow is another day," the child often repeated to herself, after the manner  of her people. That meant, "Although I am safe now, no one knows what will come next." Then Maria would sigh for a moment and look sad. But she was naturally merry and gay, and the next moment would be dancing about and humming a lively tune.

What news was her brave brother bringing this morning? As soon as he came in sight, Maria ran to meet him. The sun was very hot and the little girl's head was bare, but she did not think of these things. The Spaniards! The Spaniards! made the only picture she could see.

As soon as she was within easy call, Ramon told her that a company of the enemy was only two miles away. He had been very close to them. He had even heard them talking together while he hid in the bushes.

"Just think, Maria," he exclaimed, "they were laughing at the easy time they would have in breaking our spirit. They said that  before long they would starve us into giving up. I rather think they won't. Do you know, Maria, I believe God will send us help if we are only patient. The Americans live so near us, I don't see how they can help taking our part, when they know the way we are treated.

But come, we must hurry and tell father the news. He will know what we ought to do to get ready for a visit to-day."

The children hurried to the house, and soon every one was in a state of the greatest excitement. When Señor Diaz was told of the approach of the Spaniards, he said, in his gentle voice, "We would best have a picnic."

The children looked greatly astonished at the idea of a picnic at such a time, but their father went on to explain. He had often thought of the coming of the Spanish troops. He had made a plan in case he should hear of their approach. The house should be locked up; all the family should go down to the shore of a small lake a quarter of a mile back in the woods. The path that led to this lake was so hidden that a stranger would not know it was there. Ramon could lead the oxen; the father thought that he was strong enough to guide the horse to the picnic-ground.

If the Spaniards found no one about the house, and no animals worth capturing, they might possibly pass by without doing any harm.

Señora Diaz and old black Paulina got a hasty luncheon ready. Maria said she must certainly take her sewing materials, for she was going to embroider some insurgent emblems. Her little sister, Isabella, carried her pet kitten in her arms, and cried because the parrot must be left behind.

"He'll be so lonesome," she said; "and I just know he'll call 'Isabella' all day long."

The dear little girl cried hard, but everybody's hands were so full that Mr. Poll was left in the house. A big linen cloth was stretched over the cage. If kept in the dark, he would probably be still, and not attract the attention of the soldiers, if they stopped and looked in. The black man servant, Miguel, stayed behind to shut up the chickens in barrels, but would follow the rest of the party in a few moments.

The path led in and out through the beautiful southern woods. There were cocoanut-palms and ebony and mahogany trees, while underneath were creeping vines and bushes, making a close thicket of underbrush. There was no talking. The family crept along as quietly as possible, lest they should be heard and followed. For by this time the enemy must be very near.

# CHAPTER II

## THE PICNIC

In a few minutes the lake was in sight. It was a very pretty sheet of water. A tiny boat rocked to and fro close to the shore, for Ramon and Maria often came here to row about the quiet lake.

Ramon soon had two hammocks swinging between the trees for his father and mother. The lunch was spread out on the ground, as it was already past the time for the noonday meal.

"What did they have to eat?" you ask. There were some delicate white rolls, that Paulina knew how to make so nicely. There was guava jelly to eat on the rolls; fresh lemons and newly made sugar from which to make a refreshing drink. Besides these, there was plenty of cold fried chicken. Could any children have a nicer picnic lunch than this, even if a long time had been spent in getting ready for it?

The guava jelly looked just as clear and beautiful as that which is brought to America, and sold here at such a high price. Did you ever see it in the stores of Boston or New York, and think how nice it must taste? Perhaps your mother has bought it for you when you were getting well after a long illness, and wished to tempt your appetite by some new dainty. Maria has several guava-trees near her home. Paulina makes so much jelly from the ripe fruit that perhaps the little girl does not realise how nice it is.

After the lunch, Señor Diaz stretched himself in one of the hammocks for a quiet rest. He was very tired after his walk through the woods. He was also troubled over the sad state of things in his country, and was worried that he was not strong enough to take a more active part against the enemy. His wife lay down in the other hammock for a noonday nap, after which she promised to help Maria in her sewing.

Paulina gathered the remains of the lunch and put things in order, while the three children rowed around the lake.

"Won't you hear me read out of my primer, Maria?" said Isabella. "Ramon, dear, give your oars a rest, and float for a little while. You can listen, too, and I know you'll like my lesson to-day."

5

The little girl was just learning to read, and she had a book printed by the insurgents. No one had to urge her to study, for even her own little primer was made up of stories about the war. She had tucked her loved book in the loose waist of her dress when she left the house. No one had noticed it before.

boy looking at fort in the distance

## "'I COUNTED THREE DIFFERENT FORTS OF THE ENEMY'"

"Why, yes, my darling sister, certainly I will listen, and help you with the big words, too," answered Maria, while Ramon drew in his oars, and lay back in the boat with a pleasant smile. Of course the words were all Spanish, because that was the only language the children had ever learned. Isabella read:

"My papa is in the army of the Cubans. He fights to make us free. Do you hear the cannon roar? Our men will bring victory. Long live Cuba!"

When Isabella came to the word "victory," Maria had to help her. It was such a big word for the six-year-old child to pronounce. She looked at it again and again, repeating it slowly to herself. Then she said:

"I'll never fail on that word again, Maria, no matter where it is. How I would like to see it in great big letters on a silk banner! I'd wave it all day long."

This was a good deal for such a little girl to say, but then, you know, she was living in the midst of war.

"Good for you," said her brother; "we'll all live yet to see the words of your primer come true. Long live free Cuba! I say. But come, let's go on shore, and play war. You and Maria can be the Spaniards, and I'll be the insurgent army. You just see how I will make short work of taking you prisoners."

The children landed under a big cotton-tree. They made a fort out of dead branches which they gathered. This fort was to belong to the Spanish troops. The two girls placed themselves behind it, and stood ready to defend themselves. It was not many minutes before Ramon took them by surprise, and dragged them to the boat, which stood for the Cuban headquarters.

"Do you know," said the boy, when they stopped to rest a few minutes from their sport, "I counted three different forts of the enemy during my tramp this morning. The cowardly Spaniards don't dare to march very far away from those forts. They really don't give our men a chance to have a good fair battle. They think by having plenty of forts they can keep our soldiers from getting into the cities. Then they will scare the rest of us who live in the country from feeding them. In that way we will be starved into giving in. We'll see, that's all."

By this time Maria could see that her mother had waked up and left the hammock.

"She will be ready to help me with my work now," said Maria. "Don't you want to come and watch me embroider, Isabella?"

The two girls were soon sitting beside their mother, while Ramon went with Miguel on a hunt for birds. The insurgent emblems which Maria was so eager to make were to be given to the Cuban soldiers. They were to wear beneath their coats. Suppose that an insurgent should stop at any place, and ask for food and rest; how would the people know that he was true to his country, and not a friend of the Spaniards? He could show his little piece of flannel with the watchword of the Cubans embroidered upon it. That was the only thing needed. The people would be safe now in giving him help.

Maria did her work very nicely. She made a scalloped edge with red silk all around the white cloth. A crimson heart on a green cross must then be made, with underneath these words:

"Be of good cheer. The heart of Jesus is with me."

Two hours went by before Ramon came back. Miguel and he were bringing a large net full of birds. Of course, they had done no shooting. That would not have been wise when Spanish soldiers might be near to hear the noise. No, they had searched through the woods till they found some sour orange trees. The fruit was ripe now and there were sure to be numbers of parrots around. They could be caught in the net that Miguel had brought from the house that morning. They had to creep along very quietly so as to take the birds by surprise.

They had great success, it seemed; but what would the family do with a dozen dead parrots? Eat them, to be sure. Paulina would make a fine stew for dinner

7

that very night. That is, of course, if they were fortunate enough to find the house still standing when they reached home. The flesh of this bird is tough, and one wonders that Ramon and Maria are so fond of parrot stew. In Cuba there are many nicer birds for eating. But each one has his own tastes. No two people are alike, we have found out long ago.

"I discovered something in the woods that I want to show you girls," said Ramon. "It's only a little ways off. Won't you come, too, mamma? It's the dearest little nest I ever saw in my life. It must belong to a humming-bird."

Ramon's mother and the children followed him till the boy stopped in front of a low bush. Hidden away under the leaves was the tiny nest. It was no bigger than a large thimble. It was made of cotton, bound together with two or three horse-hairs.

"I'm sure I couldn't have sewed it as well as that," said Maria. "See how the threads are woven in and out. It's wonderful what birds can do. But look at the eggs, mamma dear. See! there are two of them. They aren't any bigger than peas."

Just then the children heard a fluttering of tiny wings. It was Mrs. Humming-Bird who had come home. She was troubled at the sight of the strangers.

"Did you ever before see such a small bird?" whispered Isabella. "She looks like a butterfly, and a small one, too. Aren't her colours beautiful?"

"We would best let her go back to her nest, now, my dears," said Señora Diaz. "You can watch, Ramon, and find out when the baby birds hatch. We shall all like to see them, I'm sure."

They left the bush and turned back toward the lake. Ramon stopped again, however, when they came to a small lace-wood tree.

"You know you asked me to get you some of the wood to trim your doll's dress, Isabella. Here is a good chance to get it. I'll follow you in a few minutes."

Ramon took out his knife, and soon the young tree was cut away from the roots. It would take some time to strip off the bark. It must be done carefully and peeled off in one piece, so as to leave the pith of the tree quite smooth and whole. Several strips of delicate lace could be obtained from this pith. Now

Isabella would be able to dress her doll in great elegance. She could ruffle the lace on the waist and flounces of the doll's skirt and make it look as beautiful as though it cost a good deal of money. Isabella herself has a dress trimmed with the lace, but Paulina needs to be very careful when she irons it. It was growing dark when Ramon arrived at the shore with his tree.

"We will go back now," said Señor Diaz, "and see if the soldiers have left us our home."

All were soon making their way back to the house, which they found unharmed. Nothing had been touched by the enemy. Perhaps they had not thought it worth while to stop. At any rate, there was great joy in the Diaz family that evening as they sat on the balcony, sipping cups of hot sweetened water. The times were so hard they could not buy coffee, and guaraba, as they called it, was the next best thing. Maria is very fond of it.

The children were so tired from the day's excitement that by eight o'clock they were quite ready to go to dreamland. Isabella started first. She went up to her father and, placing her tiny hands across her breast, looked up into his eyes with a sweet, solemn look. He knew at once what it meant. She was asking an evening blessing before leaving him for the night. Every one in the room stopped talking; all bowed their heads while the kind father said:

"May God bless my darling child, and all others of this household."

Maria and Ramon followed Isabella's example, and soon the children were sound asleep. Isabella dreamed that she taught her loved parrot to say "Liberty," and was delighted at her success.

# CHAPTER III

## LEGENDS

The next morning it rained quite hard, so the children had to stay in the house.

"What shall we do with ourselves?" said Maria. "Oh, I know. We'll ask father to tell us stories."

"What shall it be to-day?" he asked. "Do you want a tale of old Spain, or shall it be the life of Columbus; or maybe you would like a fairy story?"

"A fairy story! A fairy story!" all cried together.

"Very well, then, this shall be a tale that our people heard in Europe a thousand years ago.

"It was long before Columbus dreamed of his wonderful voyages across the Atlantic. It was before people had even thought of the idea of the roundness of the earth. They had such queer fancies in those days. Few men dared to sail far into the West. They believed that if they did so they would come into a place of perfect darkness.

"Still they had one legend of a land across the Atlantic that was very beautiful. Many of our greatest men believed in it. It was called the Island of Youth, and people who reached it could live for ever, and never grow old."

"What made them think there was such a place?" asked Maria, with wide-open eyes.

"They had heard that long ago there was a very brave young man. He had a wonderful horse as white as the foam of the ocean. Strange to say, this horse could carry him through the water more safely than the stoutest boat. As he was looking for adventure, he started off on the back of his fairy steed to cross the ocean.

"After he had travelled for some distance, he stopped to kill a giant who had enchanted a princess. When the giant was dead, and the beautiful maiden was free once more, he travelled on till he came to a land where the trees were loaded with birds. The air was filled with their sweet music.

"He stayed in this land for a hundred years. He was merry and gay all the time. He was never ill, and never tired."

"But wasn't he lonesome?" asked Ramon. "I should think he would wish for other company besides the birds."

"Oh, there were many other people there, of course, and as our traveller was fond of shooting, he had great sport hunting the deer.

"But at last something happened to make him think of his old home and friends. It was a rusty spear that came floating to the shore one day. It must have travelled across the ocean. The young man grew sad with longing for the scenes of his early days. He mounted his white steed once more, plunged into the ocean, and at last reached his own home.

"But think, children. It was a hundred years since he had seen it. His old friends were all dead. The people seemed like dwarfs. I suppose he must have grown in size and strength while away on the Island of Youth. At any rate, his own home was not what he expected to find it. He had no wish to live longer. He lay down and died. The Island of Youth had not been such a great blessing to him, after all.

"Another story used to be told in Spain of the Island of Seven Cities. It was a legend of our own Cuba, for all we know. People said that a thousand years before Columbus crossed the Atlantic, an archbishop was driven away from Spain. Why was it? He was untrue to his king. He sailed far from his country with a goodly company of men and women.

"After a long voyage they reached a land which they called Antilla. There were people already living here. They were kind and gentle.

"The archbishop divided the land into seven parts. He built churches and other fine buildings. He got the natives to help him. All lived together in peace and happiness.

"But look, children, the rain has stopped falling, and the sun is shining. You can go outdoors now, and amuse yourselves. Before you leave, however, let me ask you a question in geography.

"Cuba is shaped like what animal? Think how long and narrow it is, and of the ridge of mountains running through the centre of the  island. I will give you until to-morrow to guess the answer.

"And, by the way, did you ever think that our home is really the top of a row of mountains reaching up from the floor of the ocean? Ah, what wonders would be seen in the valleys below us, if we could journey under the water, and explore it for ourselves!"

Just as the good man stopped speaking, Miguel knocked at the door. Two ragged little girls were standing at his side. They were strangers. Where had they come from during the hard rain of the morning?

It seemed that Miguel had been tramping through the woods after game. He did not care for the rain. He was a good-natured servant, and was always ready to make pleasant surprises for the family. When he was about four miles from home, he came upon an unexpected camp. There were about thirty people in it. There, on the mountainside,  they had made rough huts to live in. There were not only men and women, but little children, also. They had been here for two or three weeks.

What a sad story they had to tell! It was the old story. They wished to be peaceful; they did not join the army of the Cubans. Still, they might possibly help them in some little way. But they did not go to the great city. They fled to the woods on the mountainside. They kept themselves from starving by gathering berries and wild fruit. Their children were sent out every morning to the country homes which were not too far off to beg for food and help.

"Poor little children!" exclaimed Maria, when Miguel had finished his story. "We will help you all we can, won't we, papa?" And the child's eyes were full of tears, as she said:

"We may be homeless like them, yet."

Isabella ran to call her mother and ask her help. Clothing was collected, and all the food the family could spare was put into baskets. It was far too large a load for the little girls to carry, so Ramon and Miguel went with them.

"What a good servant Miguel is!" said Señor Diaz to his wife, after they were gone. "So many of the blacks are lazy, and only think of their own comfort. But Miguel is always good-natured and ready to help."

## CHAPTER IV

## NEXT-DOOR NEIGHBOURS

It was a beautiful Sunday morning. The birds were singing gaily outside. Maria opened her eyes. Perhaps she would have slept longer if she had not been wakened by a sound in the next room. It was Ramon who was calling.

"Say, Maria, what shall we do to-day while father and mother are gone to church? Let's go over to the plantation. You know we've been invited ever so many times, and it is such fun watching the men at work."

"All right," said Maria, "but there's no hurry. We will wait till after the folks have gone before we start."

Just beyond the home of the Diaz children was an immense sugar plantation. It covered at least a square mile of land. The rich planter who owned it employed more than a hundred black men. It was cutting season now, and the work was carried on day and night, both Sundays and week-days. Sunday afternoon, however, was a half-holiday, even in the busiest time, and the black people then gave themselves up to merrymaking, no matter how tired they were.

people in a violate

## "THEY SAT BACK IN THE LOW, BROAD SEAT"

By nine o'clock Señor Diaz and his wife had left home in the oddest-looking carriage you ever heard of. It was a volante. There is nothing like it anywhere else in the world. It looked somewhat like an old-fashioned chaise. It had immense wheels, and the shafts were at least sixteen feet long.

We think at once, how clumsily one must move along in such a carriage. But it is not so. It is the best thing possible for travelling over the rough roads of Cuba. It swings along from side to side so easily that a person is not bumped or jostled as he would be in any other kind of carriage. But one does not see many new volantes in Cuba now. They are going out of fashion.

Señor Diaz was very proud of this carriage when it was new. It was trimmed with bands of silver. It had beautiful silk cushions. Even now, the good man and his wife looked quite elegant as they sat back in the low, broad seat. Isabella sat between them.

Miguel rode on the horse's back as driver. He wore a scarlet jacket trimmed with gold braid. He had on high boots with spurs at his heels. He felt very proud. It made very little difference to him that his coat was badly torn and the braid was tarnished. These were war-times and one could not expect new clothes.

"If the people at the great house invite you to stay till evening, you may do so," said Señor Diaz to his two older children just as he was driving away. "I know you will be gentlemanly, Ramon; and Maria dear, my little daughter will certainly be quiet and ladylike."

Away swung the volante down the road, while Ramon and Maria put on their wide straw hats and started across the fields for the rich sugar planter's home. They looked very pretty as they moved along under the shade-trees. Both were barefooted; Maria wore a simple white dress, and Ramon a linen shirt and trousers.

They reached their neighbour's grounds in a few minutes. They soon found themselves in front of a large, low house with beautiful gardens and shade-trees around it. But of what was the house made? It was of the same material as Maria's home, yet we see nothing like it in our own country. It was neither brick, nor wood, nor stone. Maria would say to us:

"Why, this is 'adobe,' and it keeps out the sun's hot rays nicely. Don't you know what adobe is? It is a mixture of clay and sand dried by the sun. Some people call it unburnt brick. It was nearly white when the house was new, but now you see it is quite yellow."

There was no glass in the window-cases. In such a warm land as Cuba glass would keep out the air too much, and the people inside would suffer from the heat. But there were iron bars across the casements; there were also shutters to protect the house from the sun and rain.

The children went in at the door, opened by a black servant. She looked kind and pleasant, and showed two rows of white teeth as she smiled at the young visitors. A gorgeous yellow bandanna was wound around her head.

15

"Come right in, little dears. Massa and missus will be glad to see you; little Miss Lucia has been wishing for company to-day."

She led Ramon and Maria into a large sitting-room with two rows of rocking-chairs opposite each other. They stretched nearly from one end of the room to the other. There was scarcely any other furniture.

A minute afterward, Lucia opened the door. She was about Maria's age and very pretty. But she was dressed like a grown-up young lady. She carried in her hand a dainty little fan, which she moved gracefully as she talked.

"Oh, I am so glad to see you," she cried. "But let us go out into the garden; it is much pleasanter there; don't you think so? I want to show you my sensitive plant. Did you ever have one?"

Maria and Ramon had heard their father speak of this plant, but they had never happened to see one themselves. They followed Lucia out on the balcony. A morning-glory vine was trailing up the trelliswork. It was bright with its delicate blossoms, pink and blue and purple. Close beside it was the sensitive plant.

"It came up of itself," said Lucia. "That is, you know, it was not planted by any one. You see its leaves are wide open now. It is keeping the morning-glory blossoms company. Perhaps they are talking together. Who knows? But when night comes it will close up in the same way as the petals of its next-door neighbour."

"Now, Ramon, just touch the leaves gently."

"Why, it acts as if afraid of me, doesn't it?" said the boy. "See how it shrinks away, even before I take hold of it. I declare, it knows more than some animals."

"Would you like to ride around the plantation? We have three ponies; so each one of us can have one," said their little hostess.

16

Her visitors were delighted at the idea. While a servant was sent for the ponies the children sat down under a royal palm-tree. It stood at least sixty feet high. Its trunk was perfectly straight. Far up at the top was the wide-spreading plume of leaves. There were no branches at the sides.

"I just love this tree," said Lucia. "It seems so strong as well as beautiful. Isn't it queer that the trunk of such a big tree should be hollow?"

"I think it queerer still that the roots should be so small and fine," answered Ramon. "Did you ever eat what is found at the top of the royal palm? Everybody says it is delicious."

"Yes, we had it boiled once for a dinner-party," said Lucia. "It was delicious, but you know it kills the tree to take it off; so father says it is almost wicked to get it. I think he is right."

# CHAPTER V

## SUGAR

By this time the ponies had been brought up, and the young riders started off.

How high the sugar-canes stood! The children could not see over the tops, even from their ponies' backs. The long, narrow leaves hung down much like our own Indian corn. Far up on each plant was a feathery white plume. The stalks were now a golden yellow colour. This was Mother Nature's sign that the cane was full of sap.

At Maria's home the cane had been already cut and made into sugar. But there were only two or three fields. Here, on Lucia's plantation, there were hundreds of acres. The  men had been working for weeks already, and it was not yet half cut.

"Oh, look, Ramon!" said Maria, "see that dear little black baby asleep between the canes. She can't be more than two years old. The other children must have gone away and forgotten her."

Ramon jumped down, and, picking up the little tot, lifted her up in front of him on the pony's back. She had been waked up so suddenly that she began to cry. But when the others smiled at her she rolled her big eyes around, and soon began to laugh. She was going to have a ride with white children, and that was a grand event in her life.

A turn in the rough road showed an ox-cart ahead. How small the Cuban oxen are! But they are such gentle, patient creatures, a child could drive them. How they pushed ahead with their heavy load!

When they were young a hole had been bored through the centre of their nostrils, and an iron ring was passed through. When the oxen were harnessed a rope was fastened on each side of this ring. The black driver held the ends of the rope, and guided the oxen. He had no whip, for it was not needed.

"Let's follow him up to the top of the hill," said Lucia. "He must carry his load to the boiler-house that way, and I do like to watch the oxen go down a steep place. There, see! The man will not even get off; he's perfectly safe."

As the heavily loaded wagon passed over the brow of the hill, the oxen squatted down like dogs, and seemed to slide rather than walk, till they reached the foot.

"Bravo!" shouted Ramon. "I'd trust such creatures anywhere. They ought to be rewarded with a good supper to-night. And now that they have reached level ground see how well they trot along. These dear little ponies cannot do much better."

The children still followed the ox-cart, and soon reached the sugar-mill. Immense machines were crushing the canes, and the sap was flowing into great tanks from which it was afterward taken to be boiled.

"What does the molasses come from?" you may ask. All Cuban children would tell you at once that it is the drippings from the newly made sugar.

Lucia's father does not sell his molasses, as do many other planters. He thinks it is not worth while. You cannot guess what use he makes of it. His work-people spread it on the ground to make it richer for the next year's crop.

His wife does not think of having it used in cooking, either, as American women do, and so Lucia has never tasted gingerbread in her life. Perhaps you feel sorry for her. Never mind. She enjoys sucking the juice from the fresh sugar-cane as well as the black children on her father's plantation; she has as much of this as she wishes, so she never misses the molasses cookies and cakes you like so much.

"Lucia, how is it your father keeps on having the cane cut?" asked Ramon, as the children stood watching the sap boiling down to sugar. "You know, don't you, a new law has been passed ordering the work stopped? It is all because the Spaniards are afraid that the poor insurgents will get food and help from the sugar planters."

large machine

### "THE MACHINES MADE A STEADY, GRINDING SOUND"

"Yes, I know," answered Lucia. "I heard father talking about it. He said he had paid the government a large sum of money to let him keep on. So he's all right. But perhaps I ought not to have said this, for it is his own business, and I should not repeat what I hear."

19

The children entered the sugar-mill, and stood watching the workers. Every one was so busy that no notice was taken of the young visitors. Here were great troughs full of the canes which were being crushed by heavy rollers; the juice was flowing fast into the tanks below. And there were the caldrons full of the boiling syrup; by their sides stood men with long, heavy skimmers stirring the juice, and taking off the scum which rose to the surface.

There were large, shallow pans close by, where the sugar was placed to cool. The air was full of the sweet smell of the sugar; the engines were clanking noisily; the machines made a steady, grinding sound, and, above all, the cries of the negroes could be heard, as they called to each other at their work.

A few minutes was long enough for the children to stay in this busy, steaming place. Then they went out again into the bright, clear air. After giving the black baby into the charge of one of the negro girls who was standing near by, our little cousins mounted their ponies, and rode slowly back to the house.

They passed field after field where men were cutting down the tall sugar-canes. How rapidly they moved along, leaving the ground quite clear, as they passed over it! Was it such hard work? They certainly bent over very much as they lifted the heavy, clumsy tools in their hands. These tools looked somewhat like long cheese-knives, only they were much thicker and heavier.

Ramon would say, "Why, those are machetes. I wish I could use one now in defending my country. Many a brave insurgent has nothing else to fight with excepting the machete he brought from his little farm. No guns can be obtained, for the Spaniards hold the cities, and will not allow any weapons to get to the Cubans. But those machetes will do great good yet."

As the boy watched the men working, he was thinking how differently he would like to use the machete, but he did not say anything of this kind to Lucia. He was just a little afraid that her father was not as anxious for Cuba to be free as he and his own parents were.

When the children reached the house, Lucia's parents insisted that Ramon and Maria should spend the day, and a delicious luncheon was now waiting for them.

"This afternoon," said the planter, "you may go over to the quarters and see the fun. You know it is a half-holiday, and there will be great good times among the blacks."

# CHAPTER VI

## THE QUARTERS

After a little rest in the garden, the children started out once more. This time they chose to walk, taking Lucia's big dog with them for company.

Even before they started, they could hear the sound of drums and shouting and laughter coming from the quarters. They did not have far to go before they came upon a crowd of black children. The boys were having a game of ball. It was so confused it would be hard to describe it. It certainly could not be called baseball, nor anything like it.

And here were the cabins, built close together. Cocoanut and mango trees shaded the little huts. Near each one was a small garden where the people raised the vegetables they liked best. Okra was sure to be seen here, for what old mammy could be satisfied with her Sunday dinner unless she had some of this delicious plant in at least one of the dishes? Here also was the chicota, much like our summer squash, and corn, on which the pigs must be fattened.

As for fruits, there were custard-apple and sour-sop trees, the maumee, looking much like a melon; besides many other things which grow so easily in the warm lands. Chickens were running about in every direction, while there seemed as many pens with pigs grunting inside as there were cabins.

How happy the people all seemed! That is, all but a baby here and there who had been forgotten by his mother and was crying to keep himself company as he sprawled about on the ground. And how grand the women thought themselves in the bright red and yellow bandannas wound around their heads!

You may be sure that all of the jewelry the people owned was worn that day. Maria could not help smiling at one young girl who had immense rings in her ears, three chains of glass beads around her neck, heavy brass rings on her fingers, and broad bracelets that clinked together on her arms. She strutted around as proudly as the peacocks near by.

They are handsome birds, but very vain and silly, like this poor black girl who seemed to admire herself so greatly. She tossed her head from side to side as she got ready to lead the dance.

The drummer bent to his work with all his heart; one pair of dancers after another took their places, and moved in perfect time with faster and faster steps. The crowd of bystanders watched them in admiration.

Under the shade of a mango-tree two black children were playing a game of dominoes.

"What a nice set it is," said Ramon to his sister. "I am going to ask them if they bought it. It must have cost quite a big sum for them to spend."

The older of the two players heard Ramon's words. He looked up with a proud smile that made his mouth stretch from ear to ear as he said:

"I made them all myself, little master. I got the wood from an ebony-tree."

"But of what did you make the white points set into the dominoes?" asked Ramon. "They look like ivory."

"I cut them out of alligator's teeth, little master. Now didn't I do well?"

This was said with another broad grin and a big roll of his eyes that made Lucia and Maria laugh in spite of themselves.

"Well, I should say so," answered Ramon.

"You deserve a medal. But can you read and write? A boy as smart as you ought to go to school."

"No, little master. But that doesn't trouble me any. I don't need any learning," was the answer. And no doubt the little fellow had no idea but that he was as well off as any one need be. He could play in the sunshine all day long and he had plenty of good food. Wasn't his mother a fine cook, though! He was right in thinking so, too, for she could make the nicest "messes" out of the herbs and vegetables growing in the little garden behind the cabin.

There were melons and plantains in abundance; salt fish or jerked beef to eat every day, and a long sleep at night on a straw bed in the cabin. Oh, life was a lovely thing! And what should the little black boy know of the cruel war and the Cuban children who had been driven away from their homes? To be sure, he had heard sad stories in his life, but they were about the old times when his people were brought to Cuba as slaves. He had listened to his father's tales of slavery, although he himself had been free ever since he was a little child.

The boy's grandfather was born far away in Africa where the sun was always hot. He had lived a wild, happy life in his little village under the palm-trees by the side of a broad river. As he grew up he hunted the panther and the elephant, and made scarecrows to frighten away the monkeys from the corn-fields. He was very happy.

But one day a band of white men took the village by surprise. They took many other prisoners besides himself. The poor blacks were put in chains and driven on board boats in which the white men had come to the place.

Down the river they sailed, never more to see their little thatched homes and have gay feasts under the palms. At last they came to the great ocean, where a large vessel was waiting for them. As they were packed away in the hold of the vessel, no notice was taken of their cries except a lash of the whip, now and then, across their bare backs.

Then came the long voyage, and the dreadful seasickness in the crowded hold of the vessel. Many died before the shores of Cuba came in sight. But when those who still lived were able once more to stand on dry land they were too weak and sick to care where they should go next.

In a few days, however, they found themselves working under masters on the sugar plantations, and making new homes and friends among those who were slaves like themselves.

The little domino player told Manuel that his grandfather worked so faithfully that after awhile he was given a part of each day for his own use. In this way he earned money enough to buy his own freedom as well as his wife's. But he had children growing up who were still slaves. He wished them to be free also.

Then came an order from the Spanish rulers that all the slaves should be gradually given their liberty. But this was not till many years after their black brothers in America had been set free by that great man, President Lincoln.

# CHAPTER VII

## HOME AGAIN

After Ramon and Maria got home that night they told Paulina about their visit to the quarters, and their talk with the little domino player. Paulina knew him well, and said he was a very bright and good boy.

"Some of those little negroes are too lazy," she declared, "but Pedro is always busy. I wish he could go to school, for he will make a smart man."

She went on to tell more of the old days. There was one story of which she was very fond. It was of a cargo of slaves who were being brought to Cuba. They outwitted their masters. This was the way they did it.

After the ship had been sailing for many days, it began to leak badly. The water poured in so fast that all hands were kept busy pumping it out. It seemed, after a while, to rush in faster than the men could get it out. The ship's carpenter went around the vessel, and hunted in every part, but could not find a single leak.

"It is the work of the evil one," cried the captain.

The slaves wrung their hands, and wailed, while the crew worked at the pumps till they were quite worn out. When it seemed as though the ship must soon sink, an island came in sight. The Spaniards quickly lowered provisions and water into the small boats, and rowed away, leaving the slaves to die, as they supposed.

But they had no sooner got well out of reach than the ship began to rise out of the water. The black people could be seen dancing about on the deck in delight. The sails were set to the wind, and away sped the vessel.

How was it possible? This was the whole story. The prisoners had gotten hold of some knives, with which they cut through the outer planking of the vessel. Of course, it began to leak sadly. But when the carpenter searched for these leaks the slaves had cleverly filled the holes with plugs packed with oakum, and he could not find them.

In this way the whole cargo of negroes succeeded in getting out of the clutches of the Spaniards. Old Paulina chuckled as she told the story and thought of the cleverness of her people.

# CHAPTER VIII

## STARTLING NEWS

It was a pleasant evening in February. The children felt gay and happy, for their father was getting so much stronger. Why, this very day he had walked with them a mile in an excursion to a cave. Miguel had told them such wonderful things about it, they begged their father to take them there. Although they lived so near, they had never happened to visit it before.

When they reached the spot, they were obliged to crouch down in order to enter the cave. The opening was merely a small hole between the rocks. But, as they crept down under the ground, the passage grew wider, and led into a large room.

"Do you suppose Robinson Crusoe's cave was anything like this?" Maria asked her brother.

But the answer was, "I don't think so; you know it was not beautiful. And see here, Maria, look at those shining pendants hanging from the roof. They are as clear as diamonds. Oh, look down beside your feet; there are more of those lovely things; they are reaching up to meet those coming from above."

"What makes them, papa?"

Señor Diaz then explained to the children that there must be a great deal of lime in the rocks overhead, and that, when the water slowly filtered through the roof of the cave, it brought with it the lime which formed in these wonderful crystals.

"People pay great sums of money for precious stones," said their father, "but what could be more beautiful than these shining pyramids! The pendants hanging from the  roof are called stalactites. Those reaching up from the floor of the cave are stalagmites. Do you suppose you can remember such hard words, my dear little Isabella? But come, children, I have something else to show you here."

He led the children to a little pond, in which they could dimly see, by the light of the torch, fish sporting about in the water.

27

"Those fishes are happy as can be, yet they are perfectly blind. I made some experiments years ago that led me to discover it. You see how dark it is. The creatures living here would have no use for eyesight, so they gradually became blind. We can only keep the organs of our body in good condition by using them."

It was no wonder the children enjoyed the day with their father, as he always had so much of interest to tell them. This evening, as they sat on the balcony, Maria was talking about the fish that lived in darkness, when Ramon suddenly exclaimed:

"Look! look! the garden is fairly alive with lights. The cucujos are giving us a display of fireworks. Let's catch them, and have some fun. Except in the rainy season, it is not often that we see so many." He ran into the house for a candle, and the three children were soon chasing the cucujos along the walks.

The light of the candle attracted the insects, then it was an easy matter to catch hundreds of them in a fine thread net. We should call them fireflies, but they are much larger and more brilliant than any insect we have ever seen.

As they floated along above the flowers, Maria said they always made her think of fairies with their torch-bearers. The light was soft and cloud-like, yet it was bright enough to show the colours of the flowers, although the night was quite dark.

"Why not make a belt of them for your waists, as well as necklaces and bracelets?" Ramon asked his sisters. "Then you can go in and show yourselves to mother. You can tell her you are all ready for a party."

"All right," answered the girls. "But you must help us, Ramon."

How could the children do such things without hurting the beautiful little creatures, we wonder. But they knew a way, as they had done them before.

Each cucujo has a tiny hook near its head, which can be fastened in a person's clothing without harming it in the least. Grown-up ladies in Havana often adorn themselves in this way when going to a party. They look very brilliant, I assure you.

It was not many minutes before Maria and Isabella were fairly ablaze with lights. Then they danced into the house to be admired by their parents.

"Now let's take them off and put them in those wicker cages you made last summer, Ramon," said Isabella. "I'm sure the poor little things are tired of hanging from our clothes. They must wish to fly around once more. They will not mind being shut up in the cages for a day or two, if we give them plenty of sugar to eat."

"All right, but I wouldn't keep them shut up long enough to make pets of them," said her brother. "I cannot help believing they would rather be free."

As he said these words, there was a step on the garden walk, and a moment later a strange man stood in front of the children.

"Is your father at home?" he asked. "I have a message for him."

Ramon hurried into the house. Señor Diaz came out and spoke with the stranger in low tones. When he went back into the sitting-room he carried in his hand a piece of paper  that looked perfectly blank. The stranger had disappeared again into the darkness.

"What did the children's good father do with that paper?" you ask.

He went quickly to his desk and put it under lock and key. Nothing could be done with it till the morning sun should light up the eastern sky.

"Then what?" you curiously ask again.

If we could have watched Señor Diaz, we should have seen him go to his desk once more, take out the precious paper, and go over it with a hair pencil dipped in a bottle of colorless liquid.

After that, we should have seen Maria running with the paper to the window, where the sun's rays would dry it quickly. Lo and behold! writing began to appear which threw the whole family into a great state of excitement. These were the words:

"The U. S. warship Maine has been blown  up. The Americans are roused. They believe without doubt that the Spaniards are the doers of the terrible deed.

29

Victory shall be ours at last, for the United States will now surely take our part against Spain."

There was no signature to the letter.

That very night Maria's household were wakened by a brilliant light pouring into their windows. It came from the burning plantation where Lucia had her home. When morning dawned there was no trace of a building left on the whole place. No person was injured, however, but Lucia and her parents went to friends in Havana. The rich planter had become a poor man in a single night.

Who had set the fire? It was probably the insurgents, who had discovered that the planter was a friend of the Spaniards and was secretly working against the freedom of Cuba.

## CHAPTER IX

### FIRST YEARS IN THE NEW WORLD

"Papa dear," said Maria, one evening not long after this, "why did our people ever leave Spain and come here to make a home for themselves? Of course, they had heard what a beautiful island it is, but was that the only reason?"

"They had indeed heard this, my child, but they also believed they could become rich by raising sugar-cane or tobacco. Great fortunes were made in the old days on the plantations here. My own grandfather was a very wealthy man.

"But you know the story of Cuba since then. The heavy taxes and the cruel laws of Spain caused my relatives, as well as thousands of other families, to lose their fortunes. We have tried to free ourselves many times but have not succeeded yet."

"Well, don't be sad, papa dear; the good time is coming quickly now, you know. We have not had as hard a time as the poor savages Columbus found here, anyway. How I do pity them!" said Maria, with her eyes full of tears.

"Yes, they had a sad time of it indeed," her father went on. "They thought at first the white men were angels and the boats they sailed in were beautiful birds that had brought the visitors straight from heaven. But they soon changed their minds.

"Columbus was greatly excited when he looked upon the plants and trees so different from any he had ever seen. He said: 'I will call this place the "Pearl of the Antilles,"' and so it has been called to this day. He also wrote of it, 'It is as much more grand and beautiful than any other land as the day is brighter than the night.'

"I suppose you know, Maria, that Columbus visited Cuba four times, and yet he never discovered that it was an island."

"I wish you would tell me more about the savages he found here," Maria said. "Of course, I know there is not a trace of them left in the land. Their hard work in the mines and the cruel treatment of the Spaniards soon killed them off. Oh, it is a wicked, wicked shame!"

"Their skins were bronze in colour, like the Indians of North America; but they did not know where their own people came from. Once they were asked this question by one of the white strangers. They only answered by pointing their hands upward. It was as much as to say, 'From heaven!'

"The women had long and beautiful hair, but the men had no beards whatever. They painted their bodies with the red earth so common on the island, and adorned their heads with the feathers of brilliant birds.

"They lived mostly in the open air, and slept in hammocks under the trees. They made their hammocks out of the wild cotton you have seen growing in the fields. The women spun and wove this into the only cloth they ever used.

"They had no gardens. They had no need to plough and plant, for nature gave them all they needed. There were many fruits growing wild then, as now. They picked the delicious mangoes, bananas, and custard-apples which were so plentiful. They gathered the yams and maize which also grew wild all over the island. What more could they wish?"

"I should think they would have liked a little meat once in awhile," said Maria, who had been very much interested in everything her father said.

lizard in tree above water, boy in background with gun

### "IT IS LIKE A BIG LIZARD'"

"Certainly," he replied, "these savages liked hunting, and often brought home game to be roasted. They were very fond of the meat of the iguana. You have often seen this reptile, Maria."

"Oh, I know," she replied; "Ramon shot one only the other day. It is like a big lizard."

"Yes, that is true. The Indians also hunted the voiceless dog, as we sometimes call the creature even now. I hardly know why the Spaniards gave it such a name. It is more like a rabbit than any other animal. There were great numbers on the island in the old times."

"You said the Indians slept mostly in hammocks," said Maria. "Didn't they have any houses?"

"Oh, yes, but they stayed in them very little, except during the rains. They built them of wood and palm leaves. They were clustered together in villages. Sometimes there were two or three hundred houses in one settlement, while several families used one house in common."

"How did they defend themselves?" Maria asked, as her father stopped speaking.

"They had lances pointed with sea shells, and wooden swords," he replied. "These were more for show than for use, for you know they were a sober, peaceful people. Such weapons would have been of little use if they had tried to fight with the Spaniards. The easiest thing would have been for them to leave the island and seek a new home. But they were not wise enough for that, although they had large canoes in which they might have travelled to some distance. They dug them out of the trunks of trees. Some of them were large enough to hold fifty men. Their oars were well shaped, but they used them only as paddles. They had no row-locks.

"They were a happy people, although quiet and serious in most of their ways. They used to dance and sing at their merry-makings, and their music was quite sweet."

"Papa dear, if you are not too tired, won't you tell me again about the great Spaniard who was entertained by the Indians? It was before they learned to fear the white strangers, and they still believed they were friends."

"Let me see, little daughter. Oh, yes, now I know whom you mean. I told you that story long ago. I am surprised you should remember it.

"It was Bartholomew Columbus, who was sent to act as governor during the admiral's absence. He passed from one place to another on the island to collect tribute from the chiefs. These chiefs had already learned how eager the Spaniards were for gold; so they gave it to the governor freely and cheerfully. That is, of course, those who had it. But if they could not give this they presented the white man with quantities of the wild cotton.

"There was one chief who prepared a grand entertainment in honour of his visitors. A procession of women came out to meet them, each one bearing a branch of the palm-tree. This was a sign of submission. After the women, came a train of young girls with their long hair hanging over their graceful shoulders.

"A great feast was spread in the chief's palace and the visitors were entertained with music and dancing. When night came, a cotton hammock was given to each to sleep in.

"For four days the feasting and games and dancing were kept up. Then the visitors were loaded with presents and their dark-coloured hosts kept them company for quite a distance as they journeyed onward to the next stopping-place.

"Could any people do more to show themselves friendly than these poor, gentle savages?
Ah! how sadly they were repaid for their trust in the white men!

"But come, we have thought enough about the past. Let us return to the present and the great things that are daily happening around us."

# CHAPTER X

## THE MERRIMAC

Every day now was full of excitement for the Diaz family. Letters were often brought to the house by some secret messenger. Each time they told of some new and surprising event.

The insurgents were braver than ever before. They dared more because they knew of the good friends coming to help them. Yes, the United States was getting troops ready to meet the Spaniards on Cuban soil. And our great warships were gathering also. They, too, were coming to help Cuba.

The great battle-ship Oregon was speeding through two oceans that she, also, might take part. The eyes of the whole world were watching her voyage, and millions of people were praying for her safety. How we love the Oregon to-day and the brave captain and sailors who brought her safely through her long journey!

One little American boy, only nine years old, felt so sorry for the suffering children of Cuba that he wrote these words:

"War, war, war on Spain,
Who blew up our beautiful, beautiful Maine.
Think of the poor little Cuban dears,
Think of their hardships, their sorrows, their tears,
Who die every day for the want of some food;
Wouldn't you be in a fighting mood?
Then hurrah! for the soldiers who nobly do fight
In the cause of the weak and for Nature's great right."

This is not very good poetry, but it shows the deep feeling of our children for their little Cuban cousins.

Maria, in her pretty little home under the palm-trees, was spared, yet, as she and we knew, there were thousands of children no older than herself who suffered and died before Cuba was free. Our little cousin was delighted when she knew that the American fleet was actually close to the shores of her land.

But the Spanish war-vessels were here too. They were lying in the harbour of Santiago. It was at the other end of the island, but news passed from one to another very quickly among the insurgents. Ramon drew pictures of the two fleets as he imagined they looked. He made new pictures every day. How he longed to see them with his own eyes! I really fear that he would have run away from home and joined the army at this exciting time, if he had not loved his parents so dearly.

Why did the Spanish fleet stay in the harbour of Santiago? Why did they not go out and meet the American war-ships? Were they afraid? It certainly seemed so. They believed they were in a very safe place. There was only a narrow entrance to the harbour. It was defended at each side of this opening, for on the left were new batteries which had lately been set up, and on the right was the grand old Morro Castle which had stood there for hundreds of years. In the olden times it had defended Cuba against her enemies more than once.

"Morro" means hill, and the fortress at Santiago was well named, for it is built on a rocky promontory several hundred feet high, at the junction of the open sea and the San Juan River.

Mines were sunk in the narrow entrance to the harbour so that, if the American ships should dare to enter, they would explode these mines and be destroyed like the Maine. It was no wonder the Spanish admiral thought they were safe in staying where they were.

Then it happened that a young American thought of a plan by which the Spaniards might be caught in a trap. His name was Lieutenant Hobson. It was a very daring plan, but he was a wonderfully brave man.

He said to Admiral Sampson, who commanded the American fleet:

"Let me take the Merrimac. It is a coaling vessel and very heavy. It has six hundred tons of coal on board. We can place torpedoes in different parts of the ship. A few men can help me sail her into the channel. When the narrowest part is reached we will fire off the torpedoes and escape from her before she sinks. That is, we will do so if we can. But the Merrimac will be across the narrow channel and the Spanish ships cannot get out. Our own ships will then be free to attack another part of the island. The Spanish seamen will have to remain where they are till they are glad to surrender."

36

Admiral Sampson had thought of many plans, but he liked this one of Lieutenant Hobson's best of all.

But who should be chosen to go with the brave man on this dangerous errand? Chosen! Why, there were hundreds who asked to share his danger, and only six could go with him. You would have thought it was some great festival they longed to take part in, if you could have seen how disappointed the men were, who had begged to go and were refused.

But no, it was a fight with death. To begin with, the Merrimac must pass the batteries and Morro Castle. She and those on board might easily be destroyed before she reached the place where the work was to be done. And then, when her own torpedoes should be fired off, how could Hobson and his men expect to escape from the sinking ship?

But they were risking their lives in the cause of those who needed their help. You and I know now that they were brought safely through all the dangers which surrounded them.

The Merrimac passed the guns of the Morro unharmed, for the Spaniards were poor marksmen. She reached the narrow channel where Hobson meant to do his great work. But a shot from the batteries knocked away her rudder, so they could not steer her across the narrow channel. Then a great mine exploded under her and tore a big hole in her side. She began to sink.

Hobson and his men lay flat upon the deck. Shells and bullets came whizzing about them. They dared not rise, even though the ship was breaking apart as the shells crashed through her sides.

At length the Merrimac had sunk so low that the water was up to her deck. A raft floated close to the men. It was one they had brought with them to help in escaping. They caught hold of the edges and kept their heads above water.

Just then a Spanish launch drew near. The  men on board were about to fire when Hobson cried out and asked if an officer were in the boat, as he wished to surrender. Admiral Cervera, the commander of the Spanish fleet, had himself sent the boat. He ordered the firing to cease and accepted Hobson and his men as prisoners of war.

When the news of Hobson's brave deed reached Maria, she could think of nothing else for days afterward. She would picture him in his cell at Morro Castle, looking out to sea where the American fleet were still cruising.

"How proud of him they must all be!" she cried to Ramon.

"They can't be any prouder of him than we are to have such friends as he," the boy replied. "Why, he will be looked upon now as one of the greatest heroes the world ever knew. I shall always be proud of Morro Castle because of his having been confined there.

"You know, we went all over the place when we were little, Maria. I believe he is kept prisoner in that part of the castle which is built over the water cave. You know we heard that he can look far out on the sea from his windows.

"Think of the dungeons underneath, where people were locked up years ago. We peeked into one of them that day we visited the fortress and I remember how dark and damp they were. I do hope Hobson is treated well and won't have to stay at Morro very long."

# CHAPTER XI

## VICTORY

It was only a few mornings after the news of Hobson's brave venture. The children were out in the garden, where Ramon had discovered a chameleon on a grass plot. It was a sunny day, so perhaps that was the reason the chameleon's skin was such a bright green.

"You know how gray they look on dull days," said Ramon. "Perhaps if I should put him on the branch of that tree, now, he would change to a brownish tint, to look as much as possible like it. He's a stupid little thing, though. If he does change colour, I don't believe he knows it himself. Mother Nature takes care of him, you know, and makes him change as a kind of protection. He has no way of defending himself, but if he is of the same colour as the substance around him, it is hard for his enemies to find him.

"Oh, dear! it makes me laugh when I think of a battle I once saw between two chameleons. They stood facing each other. Their small eyes glared as they slowly opened and shut their jaws like pairs of scissors. They moved about once a minute. I did not have time to see which won the battle; it took too long a time for them to do anything."

As the children stood watching the lizard they heard the sound of hoofs down the road. Then there was a cloud of dust as a horseman came riding rapidly along. He turned in at the driveway.

"What news? What news?" cried Ramon, who rushed to meet him.

It was an old friend of the family who had given secret help to the Cuban soldiers throughout their struggle for freedom.

"Of course, you knew the American troops had landed, didn't you? Well, run in and ask your father to come out. I can only stop a moment and I have much to tell him."

The gentleman had hardly stopped speaking before Señor Diaz appeared on the veranda. He was told about the position of the Americans not far from Santiago. They had met General Garcia, the brave leader of the insurgents. The

39

Cuban and American armies were now working together. Battles had already been fought with the common enemy.

But that which interested the children most was the story of the Rough Riders and their daring charges at El Caney and San Juan Hill. Many of these Rough Riders were men who had led a wild life on the plains in America. Some of them had no book-learning; they were not what one usually calls "gentlemen;" but they were great horsemen and brave soldiers. They feared nothing in the world.

They were commanded by Colonel Wood, and had been recruited by Lieutenant-Colonel Roosevelt, who had been out on the plains among them when a young man. He admired their spirit and was glad to be their commander now. He knew their ways. He led them up the San Juan heights when the enemy was protected by forts and shooting right and left at the Americans. But the Rough Riders charged onward with great courage and gained the summit. They took possession of the blockhouse at the top, and killed most of the Spaniards and drove the rest away. It was a glorious fight and a glorious victory.

"A few more deeds like that, and war and trouble will be ended for us," said the gentleman as he rode away to carry the good news to others.

"Hurrah for Lawton and Roosevelt!" shouted Ramon as he danced about the garden. "Santiago will soon be out of the hands of the Spaniards, and they will be clearing out of Cuba altogether. It seems as though I could not rest without shaking hands with our American friends."

The dear boy did not have long to wait, for the very next day came the news that the Spanish fleet had been destroyed. It had tried to escape out of the harbour, but had been discovered by the watchful Yankees. In a few hours all of Spain's war-ships had been sunk or driven ashore.

What was now left for Cuba's tyrants? The battle-ships of the Great Republic were ranged along her shores unharmed and strong as ever. The Spanish troops were shut up in the city without hope of escape. Surrender was the only thing possible to ward off great loss of life on both sides.

The Spanish commander made a formal surrender to General Shafter, and Spain's empire in the West Indies came to an end almost on the very spot where it had begun four hundred years before.

And now the mines were taken out of the harbour and our battle-ships could enter in safety. As our vessels glided inside one after another they made a wonderful picture. The harbour seemed alive with boats, and it looked like a floating city.

Still grander was the sight on land when thousands gathered around the governor's beautiful palace at Havana to see the stars and stripes of America unfurled. As the flag spread its folds to the breeze, the band struck up the air we love so well. It was the "Star Spangled Banner." Boom! boom! went the cannon, and thousands of American and Cuban hearts were filled with joy.

"Victory! Victory!" shouted Ramon, when the good news reached him that night. And "Victory!" cried little Isabella, who added with all her childish might, "Long live Cuba." Even the parrot echoed the words of the children. He seemed to feel that something very great must have happened, for his voice was shriller than usual.

In fact, the family could have no peace in the house, even if there were peace all over Cuba, till Master Poll's cage had been covered with a thick, dark cloth, and he was made to believe that night had suddenly fallen upon his home.

# CHAPTER XII

## HAVANA

"Children, would you like to go to Havana and visit our good friend Señor Alvarez for a week? He has invited us all to come and talk over the good fortune that has come to our land. You can have a good time seeing the sights."

Of course the children were delighted at their father's words; so it came to pass that Maria found herself, a day or two afterward, in a beautiful home in the very heart of the great city.

It was a grand house to her childish eyes. It was all of stone, covered with a yellowish stucco. It was at least a hundred years old, she was told. It was built around the four  sides of an open square, and had no piazzas on the outside like her own home. But the court inside was very beautiful. A fountain played here all day long, and there were blossoming plants standing in pots on the marble floor.

The family spent much of their time on the verandas in this court. It was far pleasanter than inside the house, where the windows were so heavily barred that they made one not used to the custom feel almost as if he were in a prison. The doors of the house were bullet-proof to make it safe against attack. There was but one entrance to the house, and that led directly into the court. Here the family carriage always stood unless it was in use.

The gentleman who lived here had one son, a little older than Ramon. He showed the children all around the city. As they went from place to place, he told them how hard his father had worked to raise money for the Cuban soldiers. His mother sold all her  jewels, that she might help, too. But they had to do this secretly, of course. If the Spaniards had discovered it, they might have lost their lives. This boy's name was Blanco. He was a fine, manly fellow, and was looking forward now to coming to America.

"I shall go to Harvard College," he told Maria. "I wish to be a minister, but I'm afraid if I do become one, I shall not feel like praying for the Spaniards."

The boy's heart was still bitter, but perhaps he will feel more kindly when he grows older.

One day he took his young friends out to Morro Castle. Havana has a hill fortress of that name, as well as Santiago. Although Hobson and his men had never been imprisoned in this one, yet the Diaz children were glad to see it.

It stood on a rocky point reaching into the sea. The great guns were still pointing out  between the masses of yellow stone. But they were silent. The American flag was waving and peace ruled in the land, although soldiers were on guard here and all through the city.

people looking at fort in the distance flying the American Flag

**"THE AMERICAN FLAG WAS WAVING AND PEACE RULED IN THE LAND"**

At the far end of the fortress was a tall lighthouse. It stood like a sentinel to stand watch against possible danger. Once upon a time a wall reached from the great fort in both directions around the city of Havana. But now there was scarcely a trace of it left.

"How narrow and dirty the streets are," said Maria as they left the Morro. "I must say I would rather live in the country, if I could choose for myself."

"It doesn't matter so much about the width of the streets," said Blanco, "or the poor sidewalks, either. Because, you know, we almost always ride. The working people are the ones who walk. But I do not like the dirt. That is all the fault of the Spaniards. They taxed us enough, but they kept the money for themselves.

"Last summer I was very sick with yellow fever. Mother thought I would not get well. She said she believed we had so much of this dreadful disease because the city is allowed to be so unclean.

"But look quickly at that Punch and Judy show! Let's stop and watch it. There is a man playing the harp to make it more entertaining."

The children leaned out of the carriage to see the show. Isabella had never seen Punch and Judy before, and she was greatly delighted. In a few minutes they moved on, but soon stopped again, for here stood a man turning a hand-organ with a monkey beside him dressed in a most ridiculous little suit of clothes. The monkey was dancing to the music. Suddenly he gave a spring and landed in the carriage right in Maria's lap.

Off came the monkey's cap into his little hands, and with the most solemn look it was held up to each of the children in turn.

"Take that, you poor little beggar," said Ramon as he put a silver coin into the cap. Down jumped the monkey and off he scampered to his master.

There were many odd sights for the little country cousins. Among them were Chinese peddlers showing the pretty ornaments which had been brought across the ocean. Once the children passed a cow that was being led home after her morning's work. She had gone with her master from house to house, stopping long enough at each place for her to give as much milk as the people wished.

The cow was followed by a man leading a long train of mules. They were laden with empty baskets. They, too, were going home, as they had left their loads at the markets in the city.

As for Maria, the dainty maiden quite enjoyed her rest at the great city house. She could lie very comfortably in a hammock while a little negro girl kept off the flies and mosquitoes with a big fan. She needed the nap in the city more than at home because she was awakened so early by the bells.

Perhaps the children enjoyed Sunday more than any other day during their stay in the city, for it was then that they visited the cathedral containing the tomb of Columbus. There were many churches and grand buildings in Havana, but none could interest the children like this.

It was not very far from the house, but they all went in the carriage, carrying with them the mats to kneel on during the service. It was a grand old stone building, overgrown with moss. There were many bells in the two high towers. They were pealing loudly as the party drove up.

"Just think how old it is," whispered Maria to her brother as they entered the building. "Blanco says that some of the bells were brought from Spain more than two hundred years ago. Do look at the beautiful marble pillars, Isabella. Isn't it a grand place?"

It was not yet time for the service to begin, so Blanco led the children to the tomb of Columbus, where his ashes had rested for so many years. It was at the right of the high altar. All that could be seen was a marble tablet about seven feet square. Above it stood a bust of the great discoverer.

"They say that Spain has asked the right to have the ashes, and America is going to let her take them. But we shall still have the tomb and the grand old cathedral where they have rested so long," said Blanco.

"Now come and admire the altar."

It stood on pillars of porphyry and was fairly covered with candlesticks, images, and gaudy decorations. Somehow they did not go well with the simple beauty of the rest of the church. But the children admired it, for they were ready to admire everything.

When the service was over, they drove out by the governor-general's palace. It was his no longer, however. The American general who had charge of the city lived here now. No doubt he enjoyed the beautiful gardens and ponds. He was very active in improving the city. Yes, the work had already begun, and in a few months Maria would no longer be able to complain of the dirt in Havana.

She could say again, but with a different thought in her busy little mind, "To-morrow is another day."

Yes, although it is but a short time since Maria's visit to Havana, even now everything is changed in the Diaz family. The good father no longer worries; he is fast getting to be a strong, healthy man. He has a fine position under the new government, and Maria lives in a new home just outside the city of Havana. She is rapidly learning to speak English, while one of her dearest friends is a little American girl who has lately made her home in Cuba.

THE END

Milton Keynes UK
Ingram Content Group UK Ltd.
UKHW011016020923
427894UK00004B/151

# Contents

CW00540361

giving
nature
a home

# Crows

**Mike Unwin**

BLOOMSBURY WILDLIFE

LONDON · OXFORD · NEW YORK · NEW DELHI · SYDNEY

BLOOMSBURY WILDLIFE
Bloomsbury Publishing Plc
50 Bedford Square, London, WC1B 3DP, UK

BLOOMSBURY, BLOOMSBURY WILDLIFE and the Diana logo are trademarks of
Bloomsbury Publishing Plc

First published in the United Kingdom, 2021

A catalogue record for this book is available from the British Library

Library of Congress Cataloguing-in-Publication data has been applied for

ISBN: PB: 978-1-4729-7177-7; ePDF: 978-1-4729-7175-3; ePub: 978-1-4729-7176-0

2 4 6 8 10 9 7 5 3 1

Design by Susan McIntyre
Maps and illustrations by Julian Baker
Printed and bound in India by Replika Press Pvt. Ltd.

MIX
Paper from
responsible sources
FSC
www.fsc.org
FSC® C016779

To find out more about our authors and books visit www.bloomsbury.com
and sign up for our newsletters

giving
nature
a home

Published under licence from RSPB Sales Limited to raise awareness of the RSPB (charity registration in
England and Wales no 207076 and Scotland no SC037654).

For all licensed products sold by Bloomsbury Publishing Limited, Bloomsbury Publishing Limited will
donate a minimum of 2% from all sales to RSPB Sales Ltd, which gives all of its distributable profits
through Gift Aid to the RSPB.

# Meet the Crows

Love 'em or hate 'em, you certainly can't miss 'em. The crows include some of Britain's best-known, most abundant and most opinion-dividing birds. Clad mostly in black (with a couple of notable exceptions), they have a conspicuous appearance, which along with their confident habits and raucous voices makes them instantly identifiable. Sadly, familiarity can breed contempt: in towns, we tend to overlook crows as just part of the urban furniture; in the country, we have long accused them of damaging crops and harming livestock. In short, crows have an image problem – and this is unfortunate, as few birds are more rewarding of our attention.

# What makes a crow?

The crow family is classified by scientists as the Corvidae and its members are known as corvids. As well as crows themselves, corvids include ravens, jackdaws, magpies, jays, choughs and other related species around the world. Many have a particularly close relationship with humans. Living alongside us, they have cemented themselves deeply within our culture, generating myths and folklore that are hundreds, or even thousands, of years old: for proof of this you need only look at our language, which is littered with expressions such as 'scarecrow' and 'raven-haired'. As we have modified our landscapes over the centuries, clearing forests and building towns and roads, many corvids have taken advantage of the new opportunities, displaying a resourcefulness that allows them to thrive where most other birds decline.

Scientists who study corvids have discovered that these birds are among the most intelligent creatures on our planet. Indeed, their brain-to-body size ratio is the equal of any in the animal kingdom other than humans. In addition to their advanced capacity for tool use, problem solving, vocal communication and other skills, their behaviour also

**Opposite:** The black plumage, intelligent eyes and formidable bill of a Raven exemplify all that people most admire – and most fear – in corvids.

**Right:** Carrion Crows adapt
from an early age to the
human environment.

suggests an emotional range barely known outside the
great apes and humans, including, for example, a capacity
for grief and empathy (see page 109).

Given these remarkable qualities, you might presume
that corvids belong to some separate, 'higher' order of
birds. In fact, they belong to the Passeriformes, the same
order as thrushes, sparrows, finches, warblers and many
other families of small bird – known collectively as
passerines. Corvids are bigger than most of these relatives,
however, with nearly all species being dove-sized or larger.
Indeed, the Raven (*Corvus corax*) is bigger than a Common
Buzzard (*Buteo buteo*) and is the largest of all the world's
passerines. Other features typical of corvids are their
largely monochromatic plumage – most temperate species
are either all black or black and white; the long wings
of most species, adapted for powerful, agile flight; and
a covering of fine feathers over their nostrils.

The success and intelligence of corvids come as part
and parcel of their versatile lifestyle. These birds are
generalists. In other words, rather than being adapted
to specialise in feeding on a particular food – like
finches with seeds, say, or swallows with flying insects
– their robust, all-purpose bill allows them to enjoy
a broad, omnivorous diet. This means they can adapt
to a wide variety of food sources – and can continue
to adapt as their environment changes around them,

**Left:** This opportunistic Hooded Crow has captured a fish.

using their intelligence to exploit whatever new feeding opportunities arise.

It is crows' appetites that largely explains the bad press they receive. In farmland, species such as Rooks (*Corvus frugilegus*) may gather in large numbers to feed on cereal crops, which does not endear them to some farmers – although the birds also hoover up agricultural pests in the process. During the breeding season, species such as Carrion Crows (*Corvus corone*) and Magpies (*Pica pica*) also turn predator on eggs and nestlings, which does not go down well with some gamekeepers, nor with lovers of garden birds. Meanwhile, many people find the appetite of corvids for roadkill and other carrion unappealing – even though, like all scavengers, they provide an invaluable natural clean-up service. The birds' reputation was not enhanced in bygone days when, during times of war and disease, human corpses were also sometimes on the menu.

Feeding, however, also illustrates some of the most impressive qualities of crows. These include a variety of problem-solving techniques, including using a selection of tools and in some cases even fashioning their own. Many species, notably Jays (*Garrulus glandarius*), are also habitual hoarders, collecting and caching food in secret hideaways, and then demonstrating prodigious powers of memory when they later retrieve it for consumption. This penchant for collecting and hiding explains the

**Above:** Rooks are the most sociable of UK corvids, often gathering in enormous numbers.

popular reputation of certain species, notably Magpies, for thieving.

Most corvids are highly sociable birds. Some, such as Rooks, nest in large colonies and many gather in large flocks outside the breeding season. These assemblages encompass a range of complex social behaviours. Individuals use a broad vocabulary of calls and body language to observe hierarchies, convey messages about food, warn their companions of danger and establish pair-bonds. They are capable of both assisting and deliberately deceiving one another, and some species even play games – such as 'king of the mountain' and 'follow my leader' – that appear to have no immediate practical function other than diversion.

Male and female corvids are similar in appearance and hard to distinguish from one another in the field. Most species establish monogamous pair-bonds and, like the majority of other passerines, are stick nesters, generally building their nests high in trees or on cliff ledges, depending on what their habitat offers. They lay anything from three to 10 eggs, the number varying both by species and by conditions. Incubation lasts around 20 days in most species, with the young fledging around four weeks later. Some corvids may live for upwards of 20 years in the wild, with records from some captive birds far exceeding that.

# British crows

The British Isles are home to eight species of corvid, a figure that represents 6.6 per cent of the world's 120-odd species. Most are either common or very common – only one, the Chough (*Pyrrhocorax pyrrhocorax*), is rare – and all range far beyond our borders across the northern hemisphere. Six species have largely glossy black and black-and-grey plumage: the Carrion Crow and its close northern relative the Hooded Crow (*Corvus cornix*), the Rook, the Raven, the Jackdaw (*Corvus monedula*) and the Chough. Distinguishing these can sometimes be a little tricky – although, with experience, the distinctive behaviour and appearance of each can be recognised. Two others, the Magpie and Jay, are strikingly different. A ninth species, the Nutcracker (*Nucifraga caryocatactes*), is a rare visitor from eastern Europe that occasionally turns up on our shores during harsh winters further east.

## UK corvid populations

The table below lists the most recent estimates of corvid breeding populations in the UK, as published by the Avian Population Estimates Panel in September 2019. The figures are collated from numerous conservation sources and represent extrapolation from trends as well as actual counts. For species where actual nests can be counted, figures are given in pairs. For others, they are given as occupied breeding territories. Populations of all British corvids are currently increasing and thus may have risen slightly since these estimates were released. Overall populations are highest immediately after the breeding season when young have fledged.

| Species | Breeding population |
|---|---|
| Jackdaw | 1.5 million pairs (2016) |
| Carrion Crow | 1.05 million territories (2016) |
| Rook | 980,000 pairs (2016) |
| Magpie | 610,000 territories (2016) |
| Hooded Crow | 285,000 territories (2016) |
| Jay | 170,000 territories (2016) |
| Raven | 10,000 pairs (2016) |
| Chough* | 335 pairs (2014–15) |

*The Chough population rises to 433 pairs when the Isle of Man is included.

# Carrion Crow
*Corvus corone*

**Right:** The Carrion Crow is the definitive corvid.

This species – commonly known simply as the Crow – is the definitive corvid, with its strutting walk, all-black plumage, strong flight and signature *caw*. It is common and conspicuous in pretty much every corner of the British Isles, except for the far north-west of Scotland, the Isle of Man and much of Ireland, where it is replaced by its very close relative, the Hooded Crow. A medium-large bird with a powerful bill, it measures 45–47cm (17.5–18.5in) in length and has a wingspan of around 1m (3ft). This makes it much larger than a Jackdaw, Blackbird (*Turdus merula*) and Starling (*Sturnus vulgaris*), the other all-black species you might also meet in an urban park or garden.

Carrion Crows aren't confined to urban settings, however, and range across virtually all habitats, from mountains and

**Below:** These maps show the distribution of the Carrion Crow in the UK (left) and worldwide (right).

beaches to forest and farmland. In the last of these, they are often confused with Rooks (see pages 14–16). The latter tend to be more gregarious, but this is not a foolproof distinction, as Carrion Crows may also gather in flocks outside the breeding season. A good look at a Carrion Crow, however, whether alone or in a crowd, should confirm its identity. It appears neater and less shaggy than a Rook, and lacks the Rook's bare face and peaked cap. It also has a less pointed bill, and generally shows a greenish rather than bluish gloss to its black plumage.

This species is the ultimate generalist, feeding on insects, worms, grain, fruit, eggs, small vertebrates (including rodents, frogs and even ducklings) and, of course, carrion. It will pursue and harass other predators, from Foxes (*Vulpes vulpes*) to large raptors, to exploit their kills, and has adapted to feed on human waste, on high streets, in back gardens and in landfill sites. Through this last habit the Carrion Crow has grown tame and apparently fearless, and it will often snatch whatever it can find from under our noses – competing with the likes of gulls and Feral Pigeons (*Columba livia*) for the best pickings.

Carrion Crows establish a large breeding territory and generally build their bulky stick nest in a tall tree, although they may also use cliff ledges and old buildings. In early spring, the female lays 3–4 greenish eggs, blotched with brown, which she incubates alone for 18–20 days. The young fledge after 29–30 days, and offspring from one year may stay with their parents the following year to help them raise the next brood.

This species is found across much of central Europe, although it is largely replaced in Scandinavia and northern Europe by the Hooded Crow (see pages 12–13). Further east, across Asia, the Hooded Crow also dominates, although Carrion Crows are found in scattered pockets and are the dominant species in Japan. In the UK, the Carrion Crow has long been one of the species that may be legally controlled, wherever it is perceived to threaten livelihoods or public health (see page 120). Nonetheless, such measures have had little effect on the bird's population. Today, there are an estimated 1 million breeding territories nationwide.

# Hooded Crow
*Corvus cornix*

**Right and below:** The pale-grey body plumage of a Hooded Crow immediately distinguishes it from a Carrion Crow, although in silhouette the two birds appear identical.

**Below:** These maps show the distribution of the Hooded Crow in the UK (left) and worldwide (right).

This species – popularly known as 'Hoodie' – is pretty much identical to the Carrion Crow except in its plumage. Rather than being all black, it sports a soft ashy-grey 'body warmer' around its neck, back and underparts. So similar are the two birds in every other respect, however, that for centuries they were considered simply two different colour variants of the same species. It was only in 2002 that scientists 'split' them, on the basis of DNA analysis (see box, opposite).

In the UK, the Hooded Crow is common in the far north and west of Scotland, on the Isle of Man and in Northern Ireland. Smaller numbers also occur in north-east Scotland. Elsewhere, it is found across the rest of Ireland, in eastern, northern and southern Europe (deep into both Scandinavia and Italy), and further east to central Asia. Some populations travel east and south in winter, and in the UK during this season visitors from Scandinavia may arrive along the east coast, as far south as East Anglia.

Hooded Crows are very similar in both lifestyle and behaviour to Carrion Crows. In the northernmost parts of their range they tend to breed later than do Carrion Crows further south. They have also evolved some specific adaptations to their habitat. Birds in coastal regions, for example, often use seaweed as a nest material and have perfected the art of dropping molluscs and crabs on rocks to smash them open.

Hooded Crows are known in Scotland as Hoodies and in Ireland as Grey Crows, and are a prominent part of Celtic folklore. Elsewhere, the bird is also known as the Scotch Crow or Danish Crow. Today, the UK population comprises some 285,000 breeding territories; up to 34 million individuals are estimated to occur in Europe as a whole.

## One crow becomes two

The Hooded Crow was originally described by 18th-century Swedish taxonomist Carl Linnaeus in his work *Systema Naturae* and given the species name *Corvus cornix*. Subsequently, its close similarities to the Carrion Crow (*C. corone*) led scientists to reclassify it as a subspecies of the latter, renaming it *C. corone cornix*. For decades, ornithologists treated the two birds as one. In 2002, however, further studies persuaded scientists that – just as Linnaeus had thought – the two birds constituted two separate species. DNA testing had discovered that, although they are almost identical genetically, they differ in a single gene responsible for coloration. This explains why the Carrion Crow is entirely black, but the Hooded Crow has its grey markings.

This separation of the two crows is thought to have arisen during the last glacial period, 11,500–11,700 years ago. Fluctuating ice cycles split their common ancestor species into two geographically isolated populations, and a genetic mutation in one led to the development of a different plumage. Since then, both have re-expanded their ranges, and in a few places (such as the Elbe Valley in Germany) their populations

**Above:** A Carrion Crow/Hooded Crow hybrid displays plumage that is intermediate between the two species.

overlap. Where this happens, individuals select mates by colour. However, hybridisation still occurs, producing offspring whose plumage is a mixture of the two. A true species is not generally thought to be capable of producing fertile hybrids. This is not yet the case with Carrion Crow/Hooded Crow hybrids, which suggests that true speciation remains a work in progress. However, these individuals – although fertile – are unlikely to find a mate and reproduce, as both species will generally reject them based on their coloration.

# Rook
*Corvus frugilegus*

**Right:** The peaked crown, shaggy under-feathers and pale base to the bill all help distinguish a Rook from a Carrion Crow.

Rooks and Carrion Crows are often confused. They appear undeniably similar in general size, colour and appearance, but the Rook is smaller: at 280–340g (10–12oz), it is on average about 60–70 per cent the weight of a Carrion Crow, and at 44–46cm (17–18in) in length, it is also fractionally shorter. Although it is also all black, its plumage carries a bluish rather than a greenish gloss and appears looser and shaggier, especially around the belly. In addition, the greyish-black bill is finer, the head appears more peaked, and – perhaps most conspicuous – the skin at the base of the bill is bare in adults, appearing white from a distance. Young Rooks can be hard to tell apart from young Carrion Crows before they develop this

**Below:** These maps show the distribution of the Rook in the UK (left) and worldwide (right).

bare face. In flight, Rooks also show proportionally longer and narrower wings than Carrion Crows.

The differences between the two birds are perhaps more obvious in their behaviour than in their appearance. For a start, Rooks are much more gregarious than Carrion Crows, breeding in large, noisy treetop colonies called rookeries that may comprise hundreds of pairs. In winter, non-breeding flocks may be thousands strong, with individuals performing impressive aerial manoeuvres as they tumble around the sky above their evening roosts in woods and plantations.

In their choice of habitats, Rooks are more selective than Carrion Crows, tending to avoid mountains, forests and moorland, and preferring more agricultural landscapes – typically lowland pasture or arable land. They often breed near people, locating their rookeries in stands of tall trees around churchyards or villages. In fields, they forage largely on the ground, striding about and probing with their sharp bills in search of worms, insect larvae and other invertebrates, as well as plant matter such as grain and fruit – indeed, their scientific species name, *frugilegus*, means 'fruit-gatherer'. Opportunistic omnivores, Rooks may also eat small birds and mammals. And like Carrion Crows,

**Below:** Rooks are especially conspicuous in early spring before the leaves have grown in their treetop rookeries.

they habitually feed on roadkill and will plunder human rubbish, raiding bins and often scavenging on town streets early in the morning.

Rooks mate for life and their colonies may last generations, pairs refreshing their nests with new twigs every spring. Courtship is an elaborate affair, with a pair performing various ritualised displays. A female lays her 3–5 eggs in late March or April. They are greenish blue, heavily blotched with grey and brown. Incubation lasts 16–18 days and the chicks fledge after another 32–33 days. In autumn, the young birds form huge flocks, often with Jackdaws and unpaired birds from previous years, and perform impressive aerial displays as they wheel around above their roosts.

Like Carrion Crows, Rooks are noisy, bowing their head and fanning their tail as they utter their call. Their *caw* is higher in pitch and less guttural than a Carrion Crow's, and generally given as a single call (the crow utters bursts of three or four calls at a time). At the rookery, Rooks make a wide variety of sounds, including clicks and wheezes, and captive birds have proved capable of imitating human speech.

Some farmers have long resented Rooks for the damage they cause to crops; in fact, the scarecrow was developed primarily to deter this species. The birds were once shot in great numbers, and the youngsters (called 'branchers') eaten as a delicacy in Rook and Rabbit (*Oryctolagus cuniculus*) pie. Nonetheless, studies have shown that Rooks do more good than harm by consuming a great number of agricultural pests, and for many people the bird's call is an integral part of Britain's rural charm. Today, around 1 million pairs breed in the UK. Elsewhere, the species ranges across most of Europe, its northern limit being southern Scandinavia, and across central Asia, east to Japan. Scientists recognise two subspecies: the Western Rook (*Corvus frugilegus frugilegus*), which ranges from the UK to southern Russia and extreme north-west China; and the Eastern Rook (*C. f. pastinator*), which ranges from central Siberia and northern Mongolia eastwards across the rest of Asia.

# Jackdaw
*Corvus monedula*

**Left:** A Jackdaw has a shorter bill than the other black corvid species.

This common, noisy bird is the smallest of the black corvids, measuring some 34–36cm (13–14in) and weighing around 220g (7.5oz). It is distinguishable from the Rook (with which it often associates) and Carrion Crow by its smaller size and more compact proportions, including a shorter bill and, in flight, shorter wings. It also has conspicuous pale grey irises and a pronounced silver-grey sheen on the back of the head.

*Corvus monedula* is now officially known as the Western or Eurasian Jackdaw, having recently been split by taxonomists from its eastern relative, the Daurian Jackdaw (*C. dauuricus*). The two species are very closely related and today some taxonomists place both in *Coloeus*, a

**Below:** These maps show the distribution of the Jackdaw in the UK (left) and worldwide (right).

distinct genus from the Carrion Crow, Hooded Crow, Rook and Raven. Whatever the taxonomy, our Jackdaw occurs throughout the British Isles, apart from the most remote parts of the Scottish Highlands. It also ranges across most of Europe, north to southern Scandinavia, and east through central Asia, with northerly populations migrating south to escape harsh winters. The Daurian Jackdaw occurs further east, in China and eastern Asia.

Jackdaws inhabit farmland, woodland, towns and sea cliffs. They are very at home around people, feeding in parks and gardens and often nesting on buildings. Like most corvids, they are opportunistic omnivores, foraging for seeds, grains, fruits, insects, eggs and small vertebrates – although studies show that their diet comprises 80 per cent plant matter, with animal food more important during the breeding season. Like other corvids, Jackdaws will scavenge from food waste when the opportunity arises, and are also small enough and acrobatic enough to exploit garden bird feeders. Their various innovative feeding techniques include turning over cowpats, riding on the backs of sheep, pecking open milk bottle tops and capturing flying ants in mid-air. In fields, they often forage alongside other birds, including Rooks, Starlings, gulls and Lapwings (*Vanellus vanellus*).

The Jackdaw is the only cavity nester among our corvids, seeking out tree holes or rock crevices and, in town, roof cavities or chimneys. It especially likes the walls of old castles and towers. Inside its cavity, a pair constructs a large nest of sticks. This may reach a significant size over the years, as more sticks are added beneath to support the platform above. The birds form monogamous pairs from their second year. A female lays, on average, 4–5 speckled blue-green eggs, which are paler than those of other corvids. She incubates them for 17–18 days and the youngsters fledge after another 4–5 weeks.

The origin of the Jackdaw's name is uncertain and historically (see page 25) was often confused with that of the Chough. The Jack- prefix may mean 'small', but it may also derive from the bird's sharp *tchack* call. Certainly, Jackdaws are very noisy, constantly calling and deploying an extensive vocabulary of posture and display as they negotiate their social arrangements. These interactions informed one of the

**Below:** Jackdaws are alert, curious and fond of perching on roofs.

most famous early studies of animal behaviour, described by Austrian zoologist Konrad Lorenz in his classic 1949 book *King Solomon's Ring* (see page 122). The species' supposed attraction to shiny objects has also, like the Magpie's, long been enshrined in folklore; indeed, the Jackdaw's scientific species name, *monedula*, is derived from *moneta*, the Latin stem of the word 'money'. The appearance of Jackdaws in culture can be traced back to ancient Greece.

Jackdaws are characterful and entertaining birds, with their bold, jaunty strut and head-tilting curiosity – traits that, alongside their ability to mimic human speech, have made them endearing pets. In flight, they are also among the most aerobatic, swooping and tumbling as they ride the wind around the towers and clifftops of their colonies, and banding together to drive out birds of prey and other predators. Non-breeding flocks may reach great sizes – upwards of 40,000 birds have been recorded in winter roosts in Sweden – and populations in northern and eastern parts of their range may migrate in large numbers to spend winter in milder climes.

**Above:** Jackdaws are often seen in noisy and acrobatic flight around the coast.

# Raven
*Corvus corax*

**Right:** A Raven's bill is very imposing at close quarters.

The Raven is an impressive bird, by any standards. All black, with a formidable bill, it measures some 60–68cm (26–27in) and may top 1.5kg (3.3lb). This is larger than a Buzzard. Indeed, in its majestic, soaring flight, you might mistake a Raven for a large raptor, with its wings spanning nearly 1.5m (5ft) from one deeply fingered tip to the other. Not only do these dimensions make the Raven by far our largest corvid, they also make it the largest of the world's 6,000 or so species of passerine.

The full name for our UK species is Common or Northern Raven, thus distinguishing it from several other raven species around the globe. The most widely distributed corvid, it occurs across the entire breadth of the northern hemisphere:

**Below:** These maps show the distribution of the Raven in the UK (left) and worldwide (right).

in the New World, from Mexico to the Canadian Arctic; and in the Old World, right across Eurasia, including Iceland, Lapland, Siberia, the Himalayas and northern India, and also in Mediterranean North Africa. Up to 11 subspecies are recognised, the largest being in the Himalayas and the smallest in the Canary Islands.

In the UK, the Raven is much less common than either crow, the Rook or the Jackdaw. It frequents largely upland and coastal areas – particularly in the north and west, where the more contoured terrain has offered safer retreats during past persecution. Although it has long been absent from much of southern and eastern England, a recent population increase has seen it return to areas where it hadn't been seen for decades. Elsewhere around the globe, Ravens are similarly associated with remote country, from rocky deserts to snowy mountains and Arctic tundra. In altitude, they have been recorded above 6,350m (20,833ft) on Everest, and in latitude, at around 80°N, nearly 1,500km (930 miles) north of the Arctic Circle. Their deep *cronk* call is often the only sign of birdlife in some of the world's wildest places.

If you hear that tell-tale voice, look up and you may see the bird overhead. In flight, the Raven shows a signature Maltese cross silhouette, with longer wings than other corvids, plus a longer head and neck and a diagnostic diamond-shaped tail. Ravens soar more often than other crows and can be very aerobatic, often diving from a great height with wings closed or performing mid-air barrel-roll 'salutes'; at close range, you can hear the tearing rush of air through their wings. They will often mob large raptors that pass through their territory – typically Peregrines (*Falco peregrinus*) along sea cliffs or, in the Scottish Highlands, even Golden Eagles (*Aquila chrysaetos*).

In the UK, Ravens tend to be more solitary than other crows and are typically seen in pairs (although in other regions they may gather in larger

**Below:** Ravens are often seen mobbing large raptors. This one is seeing off a Golden Eagle.

numbers). These pairs form lifelong monogamous bonds, reinforced every spring by aerial courtship displays. Each defends a large territory, in which they build a substantial nest of sticks, usually in a tall tree or on a cliff ledge. Ravens are among the earliest UK bird species to breed, with females laying their clutch of 3–7 brown-blotched bluish-green eggs as early as February. Incubation lasts 18–21 days and the youngsters fledge 35–42 days later. This species is also among the longest lived of passerines, surviving up to 21 years in the wild and even topping 40 in captivity.

Ravens' omnivorous diet includes everything from grains and berries to insects, small vertebrates, nestlings and carrion. In remote regions, they may tail large predators such as Wolves (*Canis lupus*), scavenging from their kills, and with their powerful bills can themselves be effective predators. Like our crows, Ravens are sometimes accused of attacking lambs and other livestock. This has long fuelled conflict with some livestock farmers (see page 62), although studies have shown that most livestock consumed by Ravens had already died of natural causes.

The brain of a Raven is among the largest known in the bird world, and in its foraging and social behaviour this bird displays exceptional intelligence. Like other corvids, Ravens habitually cache food and will collect shiny objects to impress their companions. Youngsters will play risky 'catch' games with big predators and even slide down snow banks, apparently for sheer fun. Studies of captive Ravens have proved that they have a capacity for empathy, and that their vocabulary extends far beyond *cronk* to at least 30 other vocalisations.

Ravens have lived alongside humans for thousands of years and are cemented deeply in the cultures of the north. Often emblematic of death, an association derived from their habit of scavenging battlefield corpses, they are also celebrated for wisdom and intelligence, and feature in many ancient mythologies (see page 114). Britain's best-known Ravens are surely those in the Tower of London, in whose absence, reputedly, the tower would crumble. But there is nothing better than seeing them in the wild, and today some 7,400 pairs are found across the UK.

# Chough
*Pyrrhocorax pyrrhocorax*

**Left:** A bright red bill and legs, and a high-pitched call are diagnostic features of the rare Chough.

The Chough – pronounced '*chuff*' – is much the rarest UK corvid, with a breeding population of no more than 350 pairs (excluding the Isle of Man). Once widespread, it is now restricted to a handful of locations along the west coast, notably in Wales, the Isle of Man, Northern Ireland, the Scottish island of Islay and the western tip of Cornwall. Outside the UK, it is more numerous, occurring around the west coast of Ireland, in parts of southern Europe (notably in Spain), and in a broad band from the Caucasus east across central Asia.

Another all-black corvid, the Chough is a little smaller than a Rook and a little larger than a Jackdaw, measuring 39–40cm (15.5in) and weighing on average around 310g (11oz). It is easily distinguished from these cousins,

**Below:** These maps show the distribution of the Chough in the UK (left) and worldwide (right).

**Above:** Choughs are typically seen flying along clifftops in small noisy groups.

however, by its diagnostic red legs and curved, bright red bill. Indeed, elsewhere this species is known as the Red-billed Chough to avoid confusion with its close relative, the Yellow-billed or Alpine Chough (*Pyrrhocorax graculus*).

The Chough's diagnostic, ringing *keeyow, keeyow* call draws attention from afar and may explain the origins of its name (despite subsequent pronunciation changes). Once seen, its demeanour immediately marks it out from other black corvids: on the ground, it moves methodically, picking and probing for insects and spiders with that fine red bill; in flight, it displays true mastery of the air, swooping, soaring and tumbling on long, broad, deeply fingered wings.

Choughs once occurred across many UK habitats, including towns. Today, however, they are restricted to coastal clifftops with plentiful nearby grazing pasture to provide the feeding conditions they require. Elsewhere, they are largely birds of mountainous regions, and have been recorded above 7,000m (23,000ft) near the summit of Everest. Choughs are solitary nesters, building their wool-lined stick nests in dark recesses in cliffs and sometimes old buildings. Pairs mate for life, returning to the same breeding site year after year. Females lay 3–5 greenish eggs, spotted with brown and grey. Incubation takes 17–21 days and youngsters fledge after 6–7 weeks.

Outside the breeding season, pairs join up in small flocks that feed and roost together.

Of all UK corvids, Choughs have the most specialised diet and habitat requirements. They have thus adapted less well than their cousins to changing land-use patterns, which partly explains their rarity today. Nonetheless, the UK population is currently stable, assisted by intensive conservation (see page 125), and in 2001 was boosted by the natural recolonisation of Cornwall – the first time the birds had bred there for more than 50 years. Choughs have also recently been reintroduced to the island of Jersey.

Cornwall has a deep historical association with the Chough, which appears on the county's coat of arms alongside a fisherman and a tin-miner. Indeed, the bird features widely in western culture, from Greek mythology to Arthurian romance – although in many cases, for instance in the plays of William Shakespeare, it is confused with the Jackdaw.

# Magpie
## *Pica pica*

**Left:** A Magpie's long tail and black-and-white plumage render it unmistakable.

There is no mistaking a Magpie. Were this bird a rarity, you might expect people to wax lyrical about its dapper black-and-white plumage, shot through with dazzling green-and-purple iridescence, or thrill to its cocky antics and rattling call. As it is, this highly intelligent species is a common sight across most of the UK, in town and country alike, and today, sadly, seems to have as many enemies as admirers.

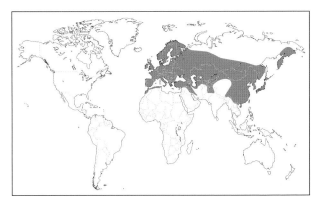

**Above:** These maps show the distribution of the Magpie in the UK (left) and worldwide (right).

At first glance, Magpies look little like our other corvids, with their two-tone plumage and long tail, but look closer at the strong bill, powerful legs and strutting walk, and you can see the family resemblance. In fact, this is one of our smaller corvids: its average weight of 200–250g (7–9oz) is no heavier than a Jackdaw, and half its 44–46cm (17–18in) length consists of tail. The rounded wings are also relatively short, and the Magpie tends to lurch and swoop across the sky without the apparent control of other corvids.

The species found in the UK is, technically speaking, the Eurasian Magpie. It occurs across the country, except in the Scottish Highlands and islands. Beyond our shores, its range extends over most of Europe and much of Asia, east to the north Pacific coast. It has also been introduced to Japan. Across this vast range, scientists recognise some six subspecies. In 2000, the magpie in North America, once thought to be conspecific, was reclassified as the Black-billed Magpie (*Pica hudsonia*), a close but distinct relative.

In the UK, Magpies typically inhabit open countryside with trees, avoiding dense forest and treeless terrain, and are common in towns and suburbs. Elsewhere, they may frequent quite mountainous terrain, and occur above 4,000m (13,000ft) in the Himalayas (where I have watched them scavenging at the leftover kill of a Snow Leopard, *Panthera uncia*). Magpies from far northern regions migrate to spend winter in temperate climes.

The Magpie's omnivorous diet comprises a broad range of both plant and animal food, including grain, fruit, acorns, insects, worms, small mammals and food waste.

The bird is a common visitor to garden feeding stations, and in suburbia its predation on eggs and nestlings has seen it take popular blame for the decline of several UK songbird species – although research has consistently proved this accusation to be unfounded (see page 61).

Magpies breed during their second year, forming monogamous pairs that occupy the same territory each season. Bonds are renewed annually with ritualised chases and displays, in which the tail is fanned and crown feathers raised. The pair builds a bulky stick nest, usually high in a tall tree, which they protect with a dome of prickly branches. In winter, when trees are bare, these nests are very conspicuous. Hedges are also sometimes used. In April, the female lays her clutch of 5–6 blue-green eggs, which are speckled with olive-brown. Incubation lasts 21–22 days, and the chicks fledge some 27 days after hatching. Parents continue to feed their brood for a few more weeks, but nonetheless chick mortality is high, with one study showing that only 22 per cent of fledglings survive their first year. Those that get through this tricky time may live up to 21 years in the wild – and potentially much longer in captivity.

The Magpie's machine gun-like rattle is today a ubiquitous sound of suburbia and often gives away a prowling cat. This is only one of their many vocalisations, however, and among other more musical sounds the birds

**Below:** Magpies will gather to feed on carrion, such as this dead salmon.

make, they can also mimic human speech. Indeed, in numerous studies Magpies have proved to be among the most intelligent non-human animals known (see page 108), demonstrating cognitive powers on par with those of great apes. Like other corvids, they can use and modify tools and have excellent memories. They have also demonstrated a capacity for grief and are one of very few species with the ability to recognise themselves in a mirror.

Wherever they occur, Magpies come laden with cultural baggage. Superstitions and folklore around the bird have inspired everything from children's playground rhymes to opera (see page 117), and the bird's supposed penchant for collecting shiny objects is notorious. Persecuted by some gamekeepers, UK Magpie populations declined during the first half of the 20th century. Numbers increased sharply after the Second World War, however, trebling between 1970 and 1990 as the birds learnt to colonise urban areas, where they faced fewer threats and were able to breed earlier. Today, the population has stabilised at around 600,000 breeding pairs, although it is still legal to control this species under licence.

# Jay
*Garrulus glandarius*

**Right:** The Jay is by far the most colourful of UK corvids.

This corvid breaks the mould. Not only is it decked out in gorgeous colours, making it one of the UK's most handsome birds, but as a shy woodland resident it is much less inclined than its cousins to flaunt itself in public.

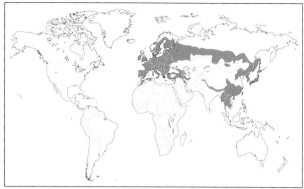

As a consequence, the Jay is surprisingly little known: many a birdwatcher will have explained to a friend that the 'beautiful' mystery bird they'd glimpsed on a woodland walk was probably a Jay.

Weighing 140–190g (5–6.5oz) and measuring some 34–35cm (13.5in) in length, the Jay is slighter smaller than a Collared Dove (*Streptopelia decaocto*) and the smallest of our corvids. But what it lacks in size, it makes up for in colour. The soft pinkish-brown body plumage is emblazoned with bold black-and-white wing markings and a striking white rump that flashes among the foliage as the bird takes flight. Flight also offers the best view of its dazzling kingfisher-blue primary wing-coverts (its 'wrists'). With a decent view of its face, you'll also notice a jaunty black moustache and a pale streaked crown that rises in a crest when excited.

This species is properly known as the Eurasian Jay to distinguish it from other jay species around the world – many of which also sport colourful plumage, often with a dash of bright blue (as in North America's well-known Blue Jay, *Cyanocitta cristata*). Like all our other corvids, it has a very wide distribution, occurring across most of Europe, north to southern Scandinavia and south to the Mediterranean coast of north-west Africa, and east through Turkey and the Caucasus in a band across central Asia to the eastern seaboard. A separate, discontinuous population occurs from the Himalayan foothills east into South-east Asia. Across this vast range, ornithologists recognise up to 33 different subspecies, each with its own variation in colour and markings.

**Above:** These maps show the distribution of the Jay in the UK (left) and worldwide (right).

**Above:** A Jay ferries an acorn to one of its autumn hiding places.

Despite the surprise it often elicits, the Jay is reasonably common in the UK – especially in areas of deciduous woodland, where its rasping screech is a giveaway, even if the bird remains hidden. It is rare in treeless areas, such as mountains and moorland, and thus absent from much of the Scottish Highlands and islands. Like Magpies, Jays now thrive in suburbia and today occur in most city parks with decent tree cover. They are also regular visitors to garden bird tables. The UK's breeding population comprises some 170,000 pairs. Numbers are boosted during hard winters by an influx of migrant Jays from eastern Europe, especially along the east coast.

Autumn sees Jays at their most conspicuous, as they fly back and forth between patches of woodland, collecting and burying acorns. Their appetite for this food is critical to the ecology of oak woodlands (see page 71). Individual Jays will bury up to 5,000 acorns each autumn, in a practice known as scatter-hoarding, and their ability to memorise the location of these caches and retrieve the acorns has provided further evidence of corvids' prodigious cognitive powers. Jays also eat other seeds, including beechmast and hazelnuts, as well as insects and small mammals. Like most corvids, they target eggs and nestlings during the breeding season.

Jays pair for life. A pair builds their nest of twigs, roots and hair deep in dense foliage in a tree or shrub. The female lays a clutch of 4–6 pale greenish eggs, covered with buff speckles. She incubates them for 16–19 days and the young fledge 19–23 days later, whereupon both parents continue to feed them for a few weeks.

As Jays are shy birds, their private lives are less well known than those of most corvids. However, close observation reveals some surprising behaviour. Jays are far more articulate than their screeching calls suggest, for example, with a wide repertoire of songs and the ability to mimic many other birds – even Tawny Owls (*Strix aluco*). They are also among the few birds known to practise 'anting', a form of grooming, in which they perch on an ants' nest and spread their wings, allowing the insects to crawl through their plumage and remove parasites (see page 98).

## A cracking rarity

In addition to the UK's eight resident corvids, a ninth species occasionally visits our shores. This is the Nutcracker, aka the Eurasian or Spotted Nutcracker. A dark chocolate-brown bird about the size of a Jay, it has strikingly patterned plumage with distinct white spots and streaks. It also sports a black cap, a white-tipped tail and a long, strong bill. Nutcrackers inhabit coniferous and mixed forests across Eurasia, from central Europe east to Siberia. They feed mainly on pine seeds, which – like Jays with acorns – they cache in hidden supplies for winter, often retrieving them later from deep beneath the snow.

Nutcracker populations depend upon the pine seed crop. When this fails, the birds – whose population rises during good times – are obliged to move elsewhere in search of food, heading mostly west and south. Such mass movements are called irruptions, and in irruption years a few Nutcrackers end up on UK shores. One such year was 1968 when more than 300 Nutcrackers were recorded here. These wandering individuals may become very tame and will feed on anything they can find, from mice to windfall apples. Irruption years are rare, and decades may pass without another Nutcracker showing up. Keep an eye out during cold winters – but don't be confused by juvenile Starlings, which are also dark with pale spots and a long beak, but much smaller.

**Above:** Nutcrackers only reach British shores during severe winters.

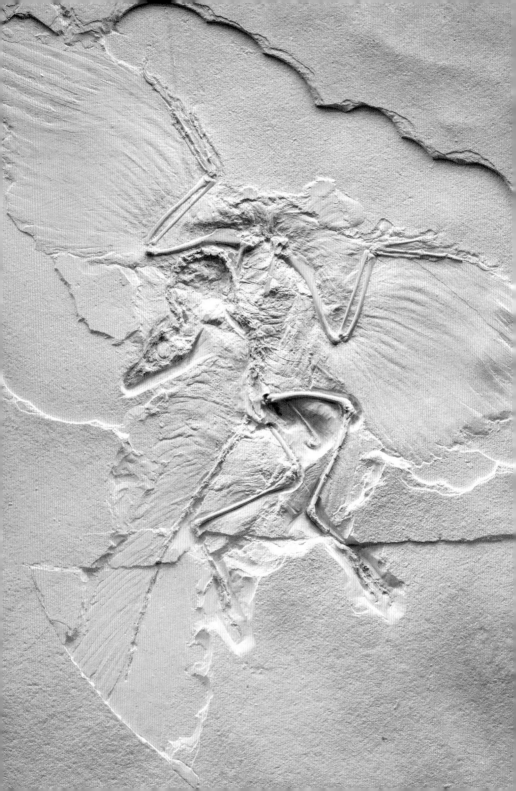

# Ancestors and Relatives

The eight species of crow found in the UK form part of the Corvidae family, which comprises at least 120 species worldwide, with multiple representatives on every continent except Antarctica. The ancestors of this family evolved millions of years ago, long before humans were around to build scarecrows and grumble about thieving Magpies. Today, crows line up in the great filing cabinet of avian taxonomy beside numerous related bird families. A tour of the globe reveals the great variety that this family has since spawned.

## Corvid origins

To understand where crows come from, it helps to consider the history of birds as a whole. The first birds evolved during the Jurassic period, 201–145 million years ago, from a group of dinosaurs known as therapods (Therapoda). An indication of their earliest forms can be seen in species in the genus *Archaeopteryx*, which lived at the end of the Jurassic period, around 150 million years ago. These famous prehistoric creatures, which were first described following the discovery of a fossil in 1861 near Langenaltheim, Germany, represent a transitional 'missing link' phase in bird evolution. They had the wings and feathers typical of all modern birds, so clearly could fly – at least after a fashion. But they also retained the teeth, tail bones and wing claws of their earth-bound ancestors.

By the end of the Cretaceous period, 66 million years ago, when dinosaurs and many other life forms were wiped out by a colossal meteorite strike, four different lineages of birds survived. These were the ostriches and their relatives (Palaeognathae), the ducks and their relatives (Anseriformes), the ground-living fowl (Galliformes) and

**Opposite:** A fossil of *Archaeopteryx*, preserved since Jurassic times, clearly shows the outline of its feathers.

**Above:** Both a Robin (*Erithacus rubecula*) and a Magpie are passerines – also known as perching birds.

what we call the modern birds (Neoaves). Among the last of these were the ancestors of the Passeriformes, which comprise the largest order of birds today, numbering more than 6,600 of the 11,000 or so known living avian species.

Passeriformes are also known as passerines or perching birds. They are characterised by an arrangement of their toes, with three on one foot pointing forwards and another (the hallux) pointing back, which allows them to grip onto perches. The passerines are divided into three subgroups, or clades. The largest of these is the Passeri (or oscine passerines), which comprises what we know as the songbirds, so named because the structure of their vocal organ (syrinx) allows them to produce diverse and elaborate songs. This is the group to which the Corvidae belongs – and, although corvids may not be renowned as songsters, most species do indeed have remarkable voices.

Tracing how crows evolved within the passerines is a taxonomic detective job that relies upon finding and interpreting prehistoric evidence around the world. The earliest fossils of 'modern' corvids originated in the mid-Miocene epoch, some 15 million years ago. Scientists now believe that the corvid lineage originated in Australasia. From here, the earliest forms moved to Asia, where they diversified and evolved into the Corvidae that we recognise today – the crows, magpies, jays and so on. These lines continued to spread, with new species evolving in Europe, Africa and America. Ironically, and relatively recently, some also returned to Australasia – their ancestral homeland – and thus gave rise to the five species found in that region today.

Faced with what we now know about the intelligence of crows, it can be tempting to imagine that the Corvidae represents a very recent branch of bird evolution – one that is somehow 'more evolved' than others. However, this would be to misunderstand the nature of evolution, which is not about progress but about adaptation. Crows' brains are not the apex of some ongoing process of refinement, but simply one avian adaptation among many in the ongoing struggle for survival in an ever-changing environment. In fact, crows are far from the most recent branch on the bird family tree and have been around much longer than many others – including starlings, sparrows and finches.

# The crow family today

The family Corvidae was first proposed by English zoologist William Elford Leach in a guide to the contents of the British Museum published in 1820. It took its name from *Corvus*, the Latin for Raven, which was the species originally described by Swedish taxonomist Carl Linnaeus in his 18th-century work *Systema Naturae*. Other species described in this pioneering work included the Carrion Crow, Hooded Crow, Rook and Jackdaw.

Today, taxonomists place the Corvidae alongside up to 54 other bird families in the suborder Passeri, which makes up the greater part of the order Passeriformes. Other families within the Passeri include such familiar birds as the larks (Alaudidae), swallows (Hirundinidae), tits (Paridae), thrushes (Turdidae), Old World sparrows (Passeridae), finches (Fringillidae) and wrens (Troglodytidae). In other words, the mighty 1.5kg (3.3lb) Raven is more closely related to the diminutive 10g (0.3oz) Blue Tit (*Cyanistes caeruleus*) than it is to the buzzards that share its mountain terrain.

Worldwide – and according to the latest taxonomic thinking – the Corvidae comprises 120 species. These fall into 24 different genera, which, in lay terms, correspond to

**Right:** A Magpie perched beside a Raven illustrates the variety in both size and plumage among UK corvids.

the following simpler groupings: the true crows (*Corvus*), the choughs (*Pyrrhocorax*), the Holarctic magpies (*Pica, Cyanopica*), the oriental magpies (*Cissa, Urocissa*), the treepies (*Crypsirina, Dendrocitta, Platysmurus, Temnurus*), the Old World jays (*Garrulus, Podoces*), the boreal jays (*Perisoreus*), the New World jays (*Aphelocoma, Calocitta, Cyanocitta, Cyanocorax, Cyanolyca, Gymnorhinus, Psilorhinus*), the nutcrackers (*Nucifraga*), the Piapiac (*Ptilostomus*) and the Stresemann's Bushcrow (*Zavattariornis*).

The largest of these genera is *Corvus*, the 'true crows'. In the UK, this comprises the Raven, Carrion Crow, Hooded Crow and Rook – those species originally described by Linnaeus. Traditionally, it also incorporates the Jackdaw, although today some taxonomists assign the two jackdaw species their own genus, *Coloeus*.

Today, corvids inhabit almost every corner of the globe, except for the polar ice caps, the southern tip of South America and most oceanic islands – although some have found their way onto oceanic islands, with several new species evolving as a result (see box on page 43). The highest numbers of species occur in tropical South and Central America, and in southern Asia, and fewer than 10 each are found in Africa and Australia. Many tropical corvids are a far cry from the all-black *Corvus* species of the northern hemisphere: they include the treepies and oriental magpies of South-east Asia, which are largely showy-looking birds with bold markings and long tails, and the New World jays of tropical South and Central America, many of which feature dazzling blues and/or purples in their iridescent plumage.

In addition to the crow species living today, at least 14 extinct species have been described. Sadly, others are also likely to disappear as we humans continue to modify and mess with the environments in which they evolved. Today, the Hawaiian Crow (*Corvus hawaiiensis*) is categorised on the International Union for Conservation of Nature (IUCN) Red List as Extinct in the Wild (although it is currently the subject of an intensive captive breeding and reintroduction programme), while another two species, the Banggai Crow (*C. unicolor*) of Indonesia and Mariana Crow (*C. kubaryi*) of Guam, are Critically Endangered.

Evolution is, however, a work in progress. Crows have proved remarkably adept at going with the flow, as evidenced by the number of species thriving in the face of anthropogenic alterations to the planet, and new species may continue to evolve. Our Carrion Crow and Hooded Crow are a case in point (see page 13): their diversification into two separate species probably began in the last glacial period, 115,000–11,700 years ago, when the advance and retreat of the ice sheet caused populations to be separated in central Europe, one of which bore a different coloration gene. Who knows what crows the future may bring – and whether we'll still be around to give them names.

**Above:** A Raven flies over a Polar Bear (*Ursus maritimus*) in the Arctic: providing evidence that corvids have adapted to some of the world's most extreme landscapes.

**Left:** A Hawaiian Crow uses a stick tool to reach food.

# Corvid family tree

The taxonomy of birds is complex, with different authorities recognising different orders, families and species. The following is a simplified summary of where UK corvids fit into the bigger worldwide picture.

**Class: Aves (birds)**
Comprises ±10,600 species worldwide

↓

**Order: Passeriformes (perching birds)**
Much the largest of the world's 28 orders of bird; comprises more than 140 families and 6,500 species worldwide (±60% of all bird species)

↓

**Family: Corvidae (crows and allies)**
One of 140 bird families; comprises more than 120 species in ±24 genera worldwide

↓

**Genus**
Five genera of corvid are represented in the UK, comprising eight species altogether

↓ ↓ ↓ ↓ ↓

| *Pyrrhocorax* | *Corvus* | *Coloeus* | *Pica* | *Garrulus* |
|---|---|---|---|---|
| (2 species worldwide) | (±45 species | (2 species worldwide) | (7 species worldwide) | (3 species worldwide) |
| Red-billed Chough | worldwide) | Western Jackdaw | Eurasian Magpie | Eurasian Jay |
| (*Pyrrhocorax* | Carrion Crow | (*Coloeus monedula*) | (*Pica pica*) | (*Garrulus glandarius*) |
| *pyrrhocorax*) | (*Corvus corone*) | | | |
| | Hooded Crow | | | |
| | (*Corvus cornix*) | | | |
| | Rook | | | |
| | (*Corvus frugilegus*) | | | |
| | Common Raven | | | |
| | (*Corvus corax*) | | | |

**Above:** The Magpie (left) and Carrion Crow (right) perch on different branches of the corvid family tree.

# Crows around the world

Corvids find a home on all the world's continental land masses except Antarctica, with some species even having managed to colonise oceanic islands. As with most groups of birds, the greatest diversity is found in the tropics, although each corner of the world has species that have adapted accordingly.

## Europe and northern Asia

All British crow species are widespread on the other side of the English Channel, with the Carrion Crow, Magpie and Raven ranging as far north as Lapland and the Raven even to Iceland. And it doesn't stop at Europe: the distribution of these species also extends from the western Palaearctic into the eastern Palaearctic, across the boreal forests and steppes of central and northern Asia – each according to its habitat requirements – as far east as Japan.

Continental Europe, however, has a few species that have never made it to British shores. The Alpine Chough, aka the Yellow-billed Chough, occurs in noisy flocks in mountain ranges such as the Alps and Pyrenees, and is a common visitor to ski resorts during winter. The Siberian Jay (*Perisoreus infaustus*) is a small pinkish-brown species of the northern boreal forests that in Europe is largely restricted

**Below left:** The Alpine Chough is a familiar sight at ski resorts in the Alps.

**Below right:** The Iberian Magpie is restricted to southern Spain and Portugal.

## Alien invader

The House Crow (*Corvus splendens*) is one of the
world's most successful corvids. Resembling
a smaller, skinnier Hooded Crow, this species
is native to the Indian subcontinent, where it
has flourished with the growth in the human
population. Noisy colonies are a ubiquitous
presence throughout its range, the birds
exploiting markets, rubbish dumps and other
feeding opportunities offered by humans. The
species was introduced to Zanzibar in 1897
and has since established a large, expanding
population in East Africa. Elsewhere, mainly by
hitching rides on ships, it has spread to Hong
Kong, Singapore, South Africa, the USA (Florida),
Saudi Arabia, Israel and even the Netherlands,
where a small colony is established in the Hook
of Holland. Large colonies of these invaders can

**Above:** Indian House Crows are particularly successful
around ports.

threaten native fauna and have the potential
to carry disease. Eradication programmes have
halted the species in some places, removing it
entirely in Australia, but elsewhere its inexorable
spread continues.

**Below:** The Rufous Treepie
is a noisy and conspicuous
Asian forest species.

to Scandinavia. And the Iberian Magpie (*Cyanopica cooki*)
is an attractive, sociable bird with bright blue wings that
occurs in the Cork Oak (*Quercus suber*) forests of southern
Spain and Portugal. This last species was once thought to
be conspecific with the Azure-winged Magpie (*Cyanopica
cyanus*) of China and Japan, and scientists had long puzzled
over why the two were found in disconnected populations
thousands of kilometres apart – until DNA testing revealed
that they were, in fact, genetically distinct.

## South and South-east Asia

South of the Himalayas in tropical Asia there are many
more corvid species. The oriental magpies are striking
birds with long tail plumes and colourful plumage, usually
with bold markings in white and/or blue. They include
the Yellow-billed Blue Magpie (*Urocissa flavirostris*) of
temperate forests in the Himalayan foothills, and the Sri
Lanka Blue Magpie (*U. ornata*), with its handsome blue
body and rufous head, which is endemic to the island
after which it is named and of which it is also the national
bird. The treepies are similar, and include the widespread

Rufous Treepie (*Dendrocitta vagabunda*), common in farmland, forests and suburban gardens across the region.

Among the all-black corvids of southern Asia, the Brown-necked Raven (*Corvus ruficollis*) is found largely in mountainous and desert regions, ranging from North Africa and the Middle East through Pakistan and the Caucasus. Better known is the ubiquitous House Crow, which resembles a skinny cross between a Hooded Crow and a Jackdaw, its black face contrasting with a grey neck and mantle (see box, opposite). This species thrives around human settlements and is a noisy resident of most Indian cities, making the most of the abundant rubbish found in urban settings. By hitching a ride aboard ships, it has also colonised several other parts of the world, where it is regarded as an unwelcome and destructive alien invader.

## Australasia

Australasia may have been the ancestral birthplace of the Corvidae, but today the region is rather short on crows. Only five species occur, all of which are typical all-black members of the *Corvus* genus, the largest being the Australian Raven (*C. coronoides*), which occurs across much of the east of the country and in the far south-west. Beware common names when down under: neither the Australian Magpie (*Gymnorhina tibicen*) nor the White-winged Chough (*Corcorax melanorhamphos*) are corvids but belong to entirely separate families, having been named by early European immigrants for their superficial resemblance to their namesakes back home. New Zealand has no native corvids, but Rooks were introduced for pest control by early British settlers and, despite subsequent efforts to eradicate them, are widespread across North Island.

**Above:** The Australian Raven has distinctive pale irises.

## Africa

Africa is less well endowed with crows than you might expect, given the continent's other natural riches. Only 11 corvid species occur, of which eight are true crows of the *Corvus* genus. The best known is the widespread Pied Crow (*C. albus*), easily identified by its black-and-white

**Above:** A Piapiac finds food from the back of an African Buffalo (*Syncerus caffer*).

plumage. This successful and adaptable species occurs in virtually all habitats except the deepest desert, and thrives around human settlements, scavenging whatever it can. Others include the huge Thick-billed Raven (*C. crassirostris*), which rivals our Raven in size but has an even heavier bill and a striking white patch on its nape. This species is endemic to the Ethiopian Highlands – which also provide a home to an isolated Chough population. Further south, in the lowlands of the same country, birders seek out the endangered Stresemann's Bushcrow (*Zavattariornis stresemanni*), a small black-and-grey Starling-like species that is the sole member of its genus. And further west, from Uganda across the savannah belt of the Sahel to Senegal, the Piapiac (*Ptilostomus afer*) is another unique species – a long-tailed all-black crow that often associates with grazing herds of livestock and wild animals.

## The Americas

Across the pond, some 15 species of corvid make their home in North America. The most widespread is the Raven, whose circumpolar distribution in the northern hemisphere extends into the New World as far north as Alaska, Greenland and Arctic Canada, and as far south as southern Mexico. Almost as widespread is the American Crow (*Corvus brachyrhynchos*), the New World equivalent of our Carrion Crow. The Black-billed Magpie is, likewise, very similar to the Eurasian Magpie and was indeed once thought to be the same species.

**Below:** Steller's Jay of western North America is a gifted vocal mimic.

It is in the jays, however, that the Americas show the greatest variety. In North America, the best-known species is the Blue Jay, a widespread and unmistakable bird with dazzling blue upperparts. In the west, the closely related Steller's Jay (*Cyanocitta stelleri*) is a darker blue and famed for its vocal mimicry, often imitating raptors to fool smaller birds into abandoning their food. The Gray Jay or Canada Jay (*Perisoreus canadensis*) is a northern boreal species related to the Siberian Jay of Eurasia and known as a prolific scatter-hoarder – as is the rare Florida Scrub Jay (*Aphelocoma coerulescens*), the only bird species endemic to the state of Florida.

Heading into the Neotropics, the variety among New World jays increases. The Green Jay (*Cyanocorax yncas*) and Brown Jay (*Psilorhinus morio*) are both abundant in Central America, their plumage corresponding to their names. Many species also sport a jaunty crest. These include the White-throated Magpie-jay (*Cyanocorax formosus*), a common species along the Pacific coast of South America, and the Tufted Jay (*Cyanocorax dickeyi*), a rare endemic of montane forests in Mexico. Further south, in the rainforests of the Amazon Basin, is a group of jays in the *Cyanolyca* genus that all display rich blue and/ or purple plumage. Typical of these is the Turquoise Jay (*Cyanolyca turcosa*), found in Colombia, Ecuador and Peru.

**Above:** A White-throated Magpie-Jay in Costa Rica (left) and Green Jay in Texas, USA (right), illustrate the colour and diversity of Neotropical jays.

## Rare island crows

Not all crows are flourishing. The world's rarest corvid is the Hawaiian Crow, or 'Alalā. Once common across Hawaii, it became extinct in the wild in 2002, the victim of habitat loss, disease and introduced predators such as the Small Asian Mongoose (*Herpestes javanicus*). Today, there are around 100 individuals in captivity and painstaking reintroduction attempts are underway. Almost as rare is the Critically Endangered Mariana Crow, confined to the Pacific Islands of Guam and Rota, where only around 50 breeding pairs now survive

in the wild. This species has faced similar threats to the Hawaiian Crow, including deforestation, feral cats and – on Guam – nest predation from the rampantly invasive Brown Tree Snake (*Boiga irregularis*). Scientists fear that a single catastrophic event, such as a typhoon or bout of West Nile virus, could wipe it out. Like many island species, both these crows evolved from mainland relatives to fill vacant island niches, but have been left with nowhere to go as humans have introduced new threats to their homes.

# An All-purpose Anatomy

A bird's appearance often tells you something about the life it leads: the hooked bill of an eagle, for example, clearly suggests its owner is a meat-eating predator. Crows don't offer such easy clues. Being neither especially large nor especially small, with legs and bills best described as average, and plumage that in most species seems more utilitarian than ornamental, they have a rather all-purpose appearance. This, however, is the secret of their success, as crows are generalists rather than specialists. Their anatomy has evolved for a life of opportunity, enabling them to keep their options open while they set about meeting the challenges of survival.

## Body basics

A crow's body is built on the standard template of all flying birds. Its skeleton is adapted for flight, being both light enough to stay airborne and strong enough to withstand the strenuous exertion of flying. The limb bones are largely hollow but supported by internal struts, which makes them both lighter and stronger than those of an equivalent-sized mammal. To strengthen the skeleton, the ribs are locked tightly together and the two collar bones are fused into the single brace that we know as the wishbone. To further reduce weight, other bones found in mammals – including the tail bones – have been jettisoned, and the heavy jawbone replaced by a beak made of lightweight keratin, the same substance as our fingernails.

While many of a bird's bones are fused together for rigidity, its shoulder joints are especially flexible to permit the flight action of the wings. The wings themselves are modified front legs or arms. The short, thick upper arm (humerus), used to power the wingbeat, is barely visible on most birds, being

**Opposite:** Strong legs allow a Jackdaw to get around with vigorous hops and strides.

**Below:** The skull of a corvid, like that of all birds, supports a lightweight bill in place of heavy jawbones.

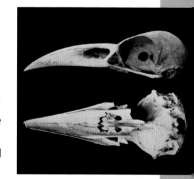

**Above:** The flapping flight of a Carrion Crow is powered by large pectoral muscles.

held close to the body. The extended wing comprises the forearm (ulna) and the hand (phalanges), which means that the joint in the middle, often seen as a backwards-bending 'elbow', is actually the bird's wrist.

A bird has little use for its wings when on the ground, so it folds them away neatly when it lands. With no hands to perform such tasks as manipulating food or preening itself, it has adapted to use its bill for these functions. This explains why most birds – crows included – have longer and more flexible necks than most mammals. Strip away the feathers from a crow's skeleton, and you'll be surprised by the length of its neck.

Another thing that might strike you about a crow's skeleton is the large, keeled sternum, or breastbone. This bone, unique to birds, can readily be seen on the carcass of a roast chicken and holds the huge pectoral muscles that are needed to power flight. By way of proof, most birds that have adapted to flightlessness, such as ostriches (*Struthio* species) and the Emu (*Dromaius novaehollandiae*), lack a keel on their breastbone.

Birds also have an enlarged breathing system, which takes up about one-fifth of their body space – as opposed to only one-twentieth or so in the average mammal. Like mammals, they breathe in oxygen and breathe out carbon dioxide. But in addition to their lungs, they have special air sacs and hollow bones that allow these gases to flow around the body more easily: thus, one bird breath goes further and does more work than one mammal breath. This means that birds have a constant supply of fresh air in their lungs, increasing the availability of oxygen to enter the blood.

Flight requires prodigious energy and birds need to move blood quickly around their system to keep their flight muscles working. To do this, their hearts are relatively bigger and more powerful than a mammal's. A crow's resting heart rate is about 224 beats per minute, about half that of a House Sparrow (*Passer domesticus*), although during flapping flight and other forms of exertion this will rise to 480 beats per minute.

# Legs: ground force

A bird's leg bones tend to be heavier than those of a similar-sized mammal. This is because a bird has just two legs to stand on and so these must be strong enough to support its entire weight. Despite appearances, its knees do not bend backwards. In fact, we cannot generally see birds' knees, which are higher up the leg, close to the belly and usually obscured by feathers. The joint we see – the one that appears to be in the middle of a bird's leg – is actually its ankle. Below this is the foot, known as the tarsus. The vast majority of birds are thus digitigrade – in other words, they walk on their toes.

Crows have longer and more robust legs than most passerines. The front of the tarsus is heavily scaled for protection and rear has a hard, protective ridge. Like other passerines, crows have three toes pointing forwards and one (the hind toe, or hallux) pointing backwards. This arrangement is best described as anisodactyl and allows crows to spread their weight evenly when moving on the ground, and also to grip branches and other perches. At rest, and even during sleep, the toes of crows and other passerines automatically tighten to prevent the bird from falling off its perch. This is because the tendons that flex the toes run along the outside of the ankle and knee, so the toes clench when these joints bend.

Birds move along the ground in different ways. Most smaller birds – and those that spend most of their time in the air – tend to hop. Larger birds, and those that spend more time on the ground, tend to walk. Hopping gets you around quicker than walking but consumes more energy. Crows, with typical versatility, do both. They will walk shorter distances when foraging for food, their relatively long legs giving them a longer stride than most passerines, but will accelerate into bounding hops if they need to cover ground fast. The one exception to this rule among UK corvids is the Jay, which spends less time on the ground than other species and always prefers to hop.

**Below:** The feet of a corvid are anisodactyl, comprising three toes facing forward and one back.

# The bill: a multi-purpose tool

A corvid's bill, like its feet, is large and robust by comparison with that of most other passerines. It is not specially adapted to any particular kind of feeding, as seen in the long, thin bills of waders, used for probing mud, or the short, powerful bills of finches, used to crack seeds. Rather, it is a multi-purpose tool that, like a Swiss Army knife, can serve many functions, including capturing insects, probing soil, foraging for grain, splitting seeds and tearing flesh. Like all birds' bills, it comprises two bony projections from the skull, the upper and lower mandibles, both covered with a thin layer of keratin called the rhamphotheca. In UK corvids, the bill varies in colour from blackish to grey – except in the Chough, which has a bright red bill.

A bird's nostrils, called nares, are located towards the base of the upper mandible – there is one on either side. Crows are unusual among birds, and unique among passerines, in having a covering of fine feathers over the nostrils, which keeps out dust. On the underside of their bill, corvids also have an expandable muscular sac called a sublingual pouch, in which they can store food while foraging. This allows Jays and Nutcrackers to carry acorns, pine seeds and other seeds to their hidden caches while building up their winter food supplies. A Nutcracker can use its sublingual pouch to transport up to 100 pine seeds in a single load.

**Right:** This Rook has filled its sublingual pouch with worms.

**Below:** A Carrion Crow's bill is a tool of both precision and power; like all corvids, its nostrils are protected by a covering of feathers.

# Feathers

Feathers define birds. Having evolved among the birds' reptilian ancestors to provide insulation, these lightweight, overlapping tiles of keratin have since adapted to multiple purposes, from waterproofing to camouflage, display and, of course, flight. Many other animals make nests, lay eggs, perform songs and even fly, but only birds have feathers.

**Above:** A Hooded Crow fluffs up its feathers to provide insulation against the cold.

On crows, feathers perform the same functions as on most other birds. Insulation is provided by tiny, soft down feathers that lie against the skin and trap a layer of warm air. More robust contour feathers overlap these to provide a weatherproof outer shell. Thus protected, crows can maintain a constant body temperature, even during extreme conditions. Indeed, some species – including the Raven – are at home in both some of the planet's coldest Arctic wastes and its hottest deserts.

Outer plumage also provides a colour palette. Some birds use subtle coloration for camouflage, while others sport striking plumage to enhance sexual selection. Most crows fall into neither of these categories, however, their plumage being either a uniform black or monochrome. Black plumage is thought to play an important role in temperature

**Below:** The black plumage of this Raven helps it shed heat in hot environments through radiation.

regulation: in colder weather and environments, it helps keep a bird warm by absorbing heat; in warm weather and environments, it helps it cool down by shedding heat through radiation.

Black plumage may also perform an important social function. Crows generally live in open environments and this colour makes them conspicuous from afar, allowing groups to keep in contact and stick together more easily. The one exception to this coloration rule among UK corvids is the Jay, which is much more colourful. Jays live in woodland, and bright colours help them to recognise one another among the dense foliage – and also to sound a visual alarm when flying away from danger.

Feathers require constant maintenance. Crows preen using their bill and – for the inaccessible parts around the head – their feet. They spread oil from a gland at the base of the tail to waterproof their plumage, and they also take regular baths. All birds moult some feathers annually, generally after the breeding season, to replace those that are worn or damaged. Most passerines moult twice a year but crows do it only once.

**Left:** A Jay's bold white rump sends a signal to its companions when taking flight.

## All white now?

You may sometimes encounter a normally all-black corvid, such as a Jackdaw, Rook or Carrion Crow, with some degree of pale coloration. Such individuals are generally leucistic: they have an inherited condition called leucism that inhibits their ability to produce melanin, the pigment responsible for black and brown plumage in birds. The effect varies from irregularly scattered white feathers to an overall washed-out or 'diluted' effect and, occasionally, entirely white plumage. Leucistic birds are often incorrectly described as 'albino'. Albinism is caused by a different genetic mutation that completely prevents melanin production. True albino birds are identified by their pink or red eyes (which lack pigment), and they are very rare in the wild and seldom survive to adulthood, as their vision is severely compromised. Leucistic birds also suffer disadvantages: their pale colours make them conspicuous to predators and less recognisable to a potential mate. Their

**Above:** Leucistic corvids, such as this Jackdaw, generally have a washed-out appearance.

feathers, lacking the strengthening effect of melanin, are also weaker and more prone to wear. Leucism does not affect the carotenoid pigments responsible for producing yellows and oranges, however. So, in some other bird species, these colours remain unaffected, and the condition is not always as conspicuous in them as it is in corvids.

# Flight

**Right:** A Raven slows down when coming in to land by tilting its wings and spreading its tail.

The other job performed by feathers is, of course, flying. This skill is made possible by the large, stiff flight feathers in a bird's wings and tail. Like most passerines, crows have 10 primaries – the largest, outermost flight feathers – on each wing. Along with the smaller, inner secondaries, these provide air resistance for flapping and taking off, and can be adjusted to offer control when airborne. The 12 tail feathers are known as rectrices and work like a rudder to provide balance, steering and braking.

The mechanics of flight are roughly the same in all birds. A flying bird overcomes gravity with an upward force, called lift, and counters drag with a forwards force, called thrust. It does this by flapping its wings: on the downstroke, the outer part of the wing tilts forwards, forcing air backwards and propelling the bird forwards, while the inner part stays level, producing lift; on the upstroke, the wing folds to minimise drag. Once aloft, the bird keeps flapping, unless it is able to glide or soar. Manoeuvring is then a matter of small adjustments, such as tilting one wing or beating the other faster to make a turn. When landing, birds first flap more slowly to allow gravity to take effect, then spread and lower their tail as a brake, before dropping the landing gear – their feet – into position.

Crows have relatively longer wings than many passerines, which equips them well for flying long distances: Rooks, for example, may travel many kilometres to and from their feeding grounds each day. They are also very agile and some species – notably the Jackdaw and Chough – are capable of impressive aerobatics, especially as they ride the updraughts over quarries and sea cliffs. Among UK crows, Jays have proportionally the shortest wings. This is an adaptation to life in the woodland canopy, enabling them to manoeuvre more easily among the branches. However, it also means they appear less fluent than other crows over longer distances, lurching with sporadic bursts of flapping in an undulating pattern rather than following the steady, leisurely flight path of a Rook or Carrion Crow.

In common with many larger birds, Ravens often save energy by soaring or gliding. Like the big raptors they sometimes resemble, they can use air currents to stay aloft for long periods of time and manoeuvre at low speeds without stalling. To gain height, they hitch a ride on thermals – the columns of warm air that spiral up from the sun-heated ground. For such large birds, however, Ravens are also highly agile, and routinely perform breathtaking tumbles and stoops during their courtship displays.

# The senses

Birds have five senses, just like humans. Their eyesight is thought to be the best of any vertebrate, courtesy of eyes that are relatively larger and more developed than those of most mammals. Birds of prey may have five times as many light-receptor cells per square millimetre in their retinas than do humans – hence 'eagle-eyed' is an appropriate epithet. This allows exceptional perception of motion and detail, and also means that their night vision is acute, which is important not only for nocturnal species but also those, such as crows, that often return to their roosts as the light is fading. As in other passerines, a crow's eyes are positioned on the sides of its head, allowing it a wide field of view with which to scan for food and look out for danger in all directions.

**Below:** The eyes of this Jackdaw, like those of all corvids, are positioned on the sides of its head to allow maximum all-round vision.

Birds also boast excellent colour vision. Their retinas have five types of colour-sensitive cone cell, compared with just three in humans, which allows them to see a richer colour spectrum than we do. The ability to perceive colours in the ultraviolet spectrum means that crows can detect plumage subtleties – for example, iridescent greens, blues and purples – that may escape our vision. A crow that may appear to us plain black is shot through with many other hues that it will use to particular effect during the courtship season.

Hearing is no less important than sight for crows. These are highly vocal birds, and their ability to perceive and differentiate between sounds is essential, given the role of social communication in their survival. Like other birds, crows do not have the external ears of mammals. Instead, openings on the sides of their head – most obvious in naked nestlings – lead to the inner ear, where sound vibrations are detected. These are protected by a covering of fine feathers known as auricles.

Relatively little is understood about birds' sense of smell. In certain specialised groups, it is undoubtedly vital: New World vultures (Cathartidae) use enhanced olfactory powers to help locate carrion at some distance, while albatrosses and some other seabirds (Procellariiformes) do the same at sea. In most other birds, including crows, a poorly developed olfactory apparatus in the brain has long suggested that smell plays a minimal survival role, although recent evidence indicates it may be more important than previously thought in helping find food and mates – and even in navigating during migration.

Taste is also generally less developed in birds than in most mammals, with taste buds not found on the tongue – which is a hard, bony organ – but in the soft tissues inside the mouth. Food passes quickly through a bird's mouth,

**Below:** This Hooded Crow in Helsinki, Finland, has a taste for cocktail sausages.

so the animal has little time to evaluate what it picks up, although it does generally receive enough information to identify the taste. Many who have reared captive corvids, however, attest to their marked preferences for some foodstuffs over others, and suggest that taste must play a role in such preferences. For example, Chicken, the Rook reared by author Esther Woolfson (see page 126), loved avocado but hated banana, and would accept Gouda cheese but rejected Camembert.

The sense of touch, however, is certainly important in crows. Like many birds, they have a spray of stiff, hair-like feathers around the base of the bill called rictal bristles, which provide additional tactile sensitivity when foraging. And while their naked legs and feet have fewer nerve endings than those of mammals, enabling them to withstand extreme cold more easily, their feathers are connected to nerve endings in the skin, giving their plumage extreme tactile sensitivity. Thus, allogrooming – when one individual bird preens the plumage of another – plays a vital tactile role in establishing and maintaining social bonds. Corvids also appear to derive tactile pleasure from anting and sunbathing (see page 98), and those who have reared captive birds attest to the great pleasure they find in taking a bath.

**Left:** A Raven allogrooms its partner, helping to reinforce their pair bond.

# Ultimate Omnivores

If it's edible, then it probably appears somewhere on the corvid menu. Versatile omnivores, these resourceful birds eat everything from fruit and cereals to eggs, insects and carrion. They are also adept at exploiting feeding opportunities that we wasteful humans have created. In perfecting the art of grabbing a bite, corvids have evolved some of the most ingenious techniques known in the animal kingdom, which explains why many are among the world's most successful birds. The one UK exception to this rule is the Chough, whose more specialised feeding requirements are the principal reason for its rarity.

# Vegetarian options

Plant food forms the staple diet of many UK corvids – especially in winter when insects and other animal foods are harder to come by. Numerous plants make up the menu, but perhaps the best known and most contentious are cereal crops, such as wheat, oats and barley. These attract large feeding flocks, notably of Rooks, which target newly sown seed in winter and spring, and forage through the stubble after the harvest in autumn. It is this allure to corvids of farmers' fields that gave rise to the scarecrow: a device designed to keep them away, and one that might perhaps be better known as a 'scarerook'. Whatever the

**Opposite:** An uncovered rubbish bin offers a world of edible possibilities for this Hooded Crow.

**Below:** Rooks settle to feed on a field of winter stubble.

**Above left:** A juicy berry provides extra nutrition for this Jackdaw.

**Above right:** Acorns are the staple diet of Jays in most areas.

species, however, most corvids are too intelligent to be fooled for long by a bunch of old clothes on a stick.

Other commercial crops targeted include peas and beans and, during harder weather, potatoes, the birds then probing the soil with their bills. Studies reveal, however, that crop damage caused by corvids is mitigated by the number of harmful weeds and small soil invertebrates – including cutworms, wireworms and grasshoppers – that they consume in the process. Indeed, it is estimated that 60–80 per cent of invertebrates eaten by Rooks are agricultural pests.

Other plant matter on the corvid menu includes nuts and berries. Windfall apples are fair game for many species, while the more agile corvids, such as Jackdaws, will pluck berries from trees such as Elder (*Sambucus nigra*). Pine seeds are the staple diet of Nutcrackers, whose longer bills are adapted to extract them from pine cones, while other corvids will break into hazelnuts, sweet chestnuts, and other larger nuts and seeds. The most prolific nut eater among UK species is the Jay, which specialises in a diet of acorns – the nut of oak trees – and has adapted to gather and cache this special food source in prolific quantities (see box on page 71). Indeed, the Jay's scientific species name, *glandarius*, is Latin for 'of the acorn'. The Jay doesn't have this diet to itself: crows, Rooks, Jackdaws and Magpies will also eat acorns, just as Jays will also eat a wide variety of other plant and animal foods.

## Pellets

In common with many birds, including hawks, owls and gulls, corvids sometimes cough up the tough undigested parts of their food in the form of pellets. The pellets of Carrion Crows and Rooks are about 2cm (¾in) across and 4–5cm (1½–2in) long. Typically, they comprise grain husks, plant stems, insect exoskeletons and small pieces of grit, and are coarser and crumblier than owl or hawk pellets, which are more tightly bound together with fur. Corvid pellets vary in colour and can be quite orange when fresh if the birds have been feeding on corn. They form in the bird's gizzard

**Right:** The shiny remains of beetles are visible in this Carrion Crow pellet.

(its muscular stomach) within 6–10 hours of a meal. You are most likely to find pellets below tall trees that serve as regular roost or nest sites. Ornithologists may collect a species' pellets over time to analyse the birds' diet without needing to kill or dissect individuals.

# Animals on the menu

A prolific variety of animal foods feature in the corvid diet. At the bottom of the scale, invertebrates – including insects, spiders and small worms – provide vital protein, especially during the breeding season when parents are feeding chicks. At ground level, this includes the likes of beetles and grasshoppers picked from the surface, or insect larvae, such as leatherjackets, dug from just below it. In the trees, Jays comb the foliage for caterpillars, while along the shoreline, crows will seek out crustaceans and molluscs. Livestock pasture is rich in invertebrate life, and many corvids will forage in and around cowpats and other animal droppings in search of the dung beetles and flies they attract.

**Below:** A Carrion Crow extracts an earthworm from the ground.

Corvids also take larger prey. Best known is their predation of bird eggs and nestlings. This habit does not go down well with some gamekeepers, who can still legally control them for taking the eggs and chicks of gamebirds such as Pheasants (*Phasianus colchicus*). Many professed bird-lovers also object to corvids' predation on garden birds: Magpies, in particular, have been widely, but incorrectly, blamed in recent years for the decline in some songbird species, and pressure groups lobby to have them controlled on these grounds alone.

With the exception of the Chough, all UK corvids do include eggs and nestlings in their diet during spring and early summer when they are, of course, feeding nestlings of their own. You need only observe how vigorously other birds mob corvids at this time of year to appreciate the threat the predators pose. The beady eyes of a crow or Magpie are highly attuned to the breeding behaviour of other species around them; they are quick to locate a nest and ransack its contents. However, studies have found no causal link between population declines in UK songbirds and increasing corvid populations – including those of Magpies (see box, opposite). Other environmental factors have consistently emerged as the principal causes of songbird declines.

As for gamebirds, it is worth bearing in mind that more than 43 million Pheasants (a non-native species) are reared and released into the UK countryside each year, vastly outnumbering the combined populations of all corvids that might predate their eggs and chicks. Meanwhile, the numbers of Pheasants killed on UK roads dwarf any natural causes of mortality (between 2013 and 2016, 38.1 per cent of reported roadkill birds were Pheasants).

A wide range of other nesting birds fall victim to corvids, with everything from Skylarks (*Alauda arvensis*) to Ospreys (*Pandion haliaetus*) losing eggs to these opportunistic predators. Hooded Crows are even known to enter the burrows of Puffins (*Fratercula arctica*) in search of unguarded eggs and chicks, while Carrion Crows have been seen plucking ducklings from the water. Corvids may also capture the adults of smaller bird species, while frogs, lizards and other amphibians and reptiles are fair game.

**Above and below:** Carrion Crows will occasionally capture small mammals, such as this Mole (*Talpa europaea*), but more often scavenge from roadkill, such as this dead Pheasant.

# Magpies and songbirds

In recent decades, the increase in the UK Magpie population has seen this species blamed for a decline in other songbirds, even prompting calls for Magpies to be culled. Certainly, some songbird populations have fallen dramatically over the same period: between 1970 and 1999, Song Thrush (*Turdus philomelos*) numbers fell by 56 per cent, Bullfinch (*Pyrrhula pyrrhula*) numbers by 53 per cent and Skylark numbers by 52 per cent, to name just three. And certainly Magpies, like most corvids, do sometimes prey on eggs and nestlings, especially towards the end of the breeding season, when they are feeding their own chicks. So far, however, numerous studies commissioned by the RSPB and others, including an analysis of 35 years of data, have found no correlation between the Magpie population increases and other songbird declines. Instead, they have established that these declines are caused by an intensification in UK farming practices – with an associated rise in pesticide use, removal of hedgerows, and a switch from spring to autumn sowing – which has significantly reduced feeding and nesting opportunities for many species.

Basic ecology dictates that, under natural conditions, predators do not control prey numbers. Instead, the converse is the norm: predator numbers are dictated by the availability of prey. The loss of nestlings and eggs to predators is built into the reproductive strategy of all songbirds, which is why they produce much larger clutches than they can generally raise. Those lost to predators form part of the 'sustainable surplus'. Predation by corvids can seem especially brutal, especially when it happens in front of your eyes in your own back garden, but it is worth remembering that all birds take life of one form or another to survive, and that fewer than 25 per cent of Magpie chicks themselves survive to their second year.

**Above:** A Magpie makes off with a Pheasant's egg.

Even small mammals sometimes make the menu: crows, Rooks, Jackdaws and Magpies take mice and voles, Jays may capture bats from their woodland roosts, and young Rabbits fall prey to crows and Ravens. The latter, with their great size and powerful bill, are the most predatory of the crow family – especially individuals living in northern tundra regions, where rodents (typically lemmings) may constitute up to half their diet.

In a few locations around the world, predation by corvids has posed a threat to particular species. Ravens in North America have been implicated in the decline of rare Marbled Murrelets (*Brachyramphus marmoratus*) and Least Terns (*Sternula antillarum*), and have even hindered the reintroduction success of the huge California Condor (*Gymnogyps californianus*), one of the world's largest flying birds. However, the rarity of these species already reflected a variety of other factors.

Predation by corvids is most contentious when it involves livestock. The largest prey known to fall victim to corvids are lambs – and even, on rare occasions, injured adult sheep. This is an emotive issue that has long led the birds into conflict with some livestock farmers, and seen them typecast as cruel villains. Under certain conditions, there's no denying that the larger corvids – notably crows and Ravens – may attack newborn lambs, typically targeting the eyes and tongue. Most research, however, has found that the vast majority of such attacks are on animals already weakened or abandoned and destined not to survive anyway (see box, below).

## Lambs to the slaughter?

Some sheep farmers have long been at logger-heads with corvids over their attacks on lambs. The birds stand accused of ugly crimes: specifically, of pecking out the eyes and tongue of the helpless youngsters, which either die a lingering death or must be destroyed by the farmer. They are even sometimes accused of attacking defenceless adult sheep that have become trapped or stuck while giving birth. It's true: Carrion Crows, Hooded Crows and Ravens may all behave in this way. However, the impact of the birds on a healthy flock remains a matter of debate. While some sheep farmers blame corvids for heavy losses, studies suggest that the vast majority of lambs targeted are either already dead or in such poor condition – sick or abandoned – that they are 'non-viable' animals that would soon have died anyway. In a 1977 study of attacks by Hooded Crows near Oban in the West Highlands, scientists found that only 17 per cent of lambs targeted were alive, and only one in 850 was healthy. Such attacks are most frequent on remote hill farms and during heavy winters when livestock losses are naturally higher. Even with improved modern animal husbandry, however, the issue persists: the recent recovery in Raven numbers has led to renewed accusations of attacks by these birds on sheep in several locations, including the Isle of Wight.

**Above:** Ravens gather to scavenge from a sheep carcass.

# Waste not, want not

Carrion of all kinds is a food source for all UK corvids – although to a lesser extent for Jays and Choughs. Anything dead, be it bird, mammal, fish or reptile, is fair game. The birds are not deterred by putrefaction. On the contrary, because they lack a raptor's hooked bill and sharp talons for breaking through the skin of dead animals, the more crushed and decomposed the carcass, the better. What's more, carcasses are often riddled with maggots, carrion beetles and other scavenging invertebrates – extra goodies.

An abundant source of such carcasses is roadkill, and corvids hopping around a verge or hard shoulder, feasting on a squashed Pheasant or Rabbit, are a familiar sight in our countryside. Indeed, a study of Ravens has shown that those nesting near roads enjoy greater breeding success than those further away because of the ready supply of roadkill. In wilder regions, carrion may form a more significant part of the diet of many species. Here, corvids often tail larger predators, such as Golden Eagles or – outside the UK – Wolves, aiming to plunder what they can from the animal's kill and benefit from its superior ability to open up a large carcass. Magpies are especially bold in such circumstances, often hopping within

**Below:** A White-tailed Eagle stands guard over a fox carcass while Hooded Crows await an opportunity to feed.

**Above:** Carrion Crows ransack an open litter bin in a public park.

inches of an eagle to grab an unguarded morsel, trusting to their superior agility to escape any lashing talons.

Even we humans are fair game. In the past, during times of plague and warfare, corvids were often seen feeding on unburied corpses. This association with human mortality is largely responsible for the sinister reputation that the family as a whole still has (see page 113), although – like any scavengers – birds behaving in this way are simply providing a vital natural clean-up service.

Today, we prefer not to leave our corpses out for corvids. However, we do offer alternative leftovers in the form of food waste and other rubbish left outside our homes and around towns. Almost all edible household waste, from potato peelings to dog-food tins, is a potential meal for a corvid, and the birds' readiness to exploit these feeding opportunities has seen them thrive in suburbia where other birds have declined.

Motorway service stations can be particularly productive places in which to watch crows, Rooks, Jackdaws or Magpies working through discarded sandwich wrappers or over-stuffed bins – especially early in the morning when they can set to the task with less disturbance. They also gather in large numbers at municipal waste dumps, often competing with similarly minded gulls, and around farms and game pens they are adept at hoovering up spilt grain from feed stores.

## Picky eater

The Chough is the most specialised feeder among the UK corvids. It eats mostly small invertebrates, including ants, beetles, emerging flies and spiders, which it picks from the ground with its fine, pointed bill – occasionally probing beneath the surface for grubs or picking maggots from animal dung. To satisfy this diet, it has very specific habitat requirements: namely, short grass, ideally less than 5cm (2in) deep, which typically has been grazed by sheep or Rabbits. It may also forage on beaches.

Elsewhere in the world – for example, in the Himalayas – Choughs habitually take fallen grain, and flocks may damage crops. In the UK, however, this species has not shown the ability of its corvid cousins to adapt to human environments. The loss of its ideal habitat to a changing agricultural landscape is thought to explain the species' decline in the UK over the last few centuries, and it is the restoration of this habitat that forms the focus of conservation efforts.

**Above:** Choughs have very specific feeding requirements.

# Feeding techniques

As well as eating a prodigious variety of food, corvids employ an impressive range of techniques to get hold of it. On open ground, long-billed Rooks pick and probe, while shorter-billed Jackdaws are adept at turning over clods in search of goodies underneath and will capture flies around dung by jumping up to seize them on the wing. These ground feeders work together in flocks and often forage alongside other species, including Starlings, Lapwings and gulls – all benefitting when one of them finds a rich source of food. Large gatherings form behind ploughs, seizing upon the larvae and worms turned up in the newly exposed soil.

For corvids, however, feeding is not simply a question of see it and grab it, and the various species have evolved many sophisticated techniques. Hooded Crows, for example, will drop crabs and bivalves from a height to crack open their shells on the rocks below. Jackdaws and Magpies, meanwhile, will hitch a ride on the back of sheep to spy insects disturbed around the herbivores' feet.

Some methods display a problem-solving ingenuity seen in very few other animals: Hooded Crows will place bread on the water's surface as a bait with which to capture fish; Ravens may pull in a fisherman's line in order

**Below:** Rooks flock to fresh soil turned by a plough.

**Left:** A Hooded Crow drops a marine mollusc on rocks to break open its shell.

**Left:** A Carrion Crow feeds beside a young Herring Gull, both searching for invertebrates in a cow pasture.

to take the fish hooked on the end; and several species will use twigs as tools to prise or lure grubs out of crevices. Among the last of these, the New Caledonian Crow (*Corvus moneduloides*), native to the Pacific islands of New Caledonia, has taken things a step further and astonished zoologists by fashioning its own tools (see page 103).

Cooperation is often the key to more complex foraging endeavours. On a university campus in Japan, Carrion Crows have learned to crack open walnuts by waiting until traffic lights turn red and then placing the nuts beneath the wheels of the stationary traffic. When the lights change, the cars move forward and crack open the nuts, allowing the birds to swoop down and retrieve the spoils as soon as the coast is clear. At a British motorway service station, Rooks have been observed getting at a partly full rubbish bin by pulling up its plastic lining in folds, one bird securing a

**Above:** Young Ravens at a carcass call loudly to recruit others.

little more with its feet while another winched up the next section, until finally the contents were raised within reach.

Working together also helps when scavenging. At large carcasses, crows, Ravens and Magpies will often team up to harass a larger predator, distracting it for long enough to steal in and sneak some food. In Scandinavia, young Ravens at such a carcass have been observed 'recruiting' helpers, their piercing yells gathering others from far and wide so that their greater numbers will help overwhelm the predator. In the process, they can also gain the upper hand on older, territorial Ravens that might otherwise drive the youngsters away. Ravens in parts of North America are thought to work commensally with Wolves, using their raucous, far-carrying calls to alert a pack to a large carcass in the snow – or even, it is thought, leading them to potential prey, such as Caribou (*Rangifer tarandus*). A woman working in her yard in a remote part of British Columbia, Canada, has told the story of how the call of a Raven alerted her to the presence of a Cougar (*Puma concolor*) that was stalking her. She credits the bird with saving her life. An alternative – and rather more alarming – scientific explanation might be that the Raven was leading the big cat to prey in the hope it would be able to grab some leftovers.

# Hide and seek

Among the best-known habits of corvids is their propensity to hide food in secret places for later consumption. This practice, called caching or hoarding, is known from a few other avian families – including woodpeckers (Picidae), tits (Paridae), hawks (Accipitridae) and falcons (Falconidae) – and is associated with advanced intelligence (see page 101). Corvids are scatter-hoarders, which means that rather than using a single repository, they cache their food in many different hideaways and must use a highly accurate spatial memory to retrieve it later.

This habit of hiding things explains the reputation of certain corvids, notably Magpies and Jackdaws, for 'stealing' jewellery and other valuable objects, although there is no scientific evidence that they are attracted to shiny things (see page 118). Nor is this behaviour limited to Magpies and Jackdaws: Hooded Crows have been observed hiding nuts under rain gutters, flowerpots and bushes, while Ravens cache food in rocks and crevices. In her 2008 book *Corvus: A Life with Birds*, Esther Woolfson describes how Chicken, her hand-reared Rook, was an obsessive cacher of food around the house. The bird would hide bits of fish, meat and cheese under cushions and rugs, in holes in the wall and even in the hems of Woolfson's clothing, often first wrapping the items in newspaper. The author's hand-reared Magpie Spike would also steal fresh dough and conceal it in the folds of a tea towel. Both birds continually moved their stashes from one location to another.

**Left:** All corvids may cache food. Here a Rook carries away an acorn.

**Above:** Ravens feeding side by side are both competitors and companions.

Not only do corvids cache food, but they also steal food from the caches of others. They will do this to other species – Ravens in northern regions, for example, will often raid the food stores of Arctic Foxes (*Vulpes lagopus*) – but also to other individuals of their own kind. Stealing food in this way is known as kleptoparasitism. It may involve a process of covert surveillance, the thief memorising the location of the cache and then returning at a later date when it can complete the heist undetected. By contrast, corvids will also often share their food with their companions, using 'active giving' as a form of social bonding.

The champion scatter-hoarders of the Corvidae are undoubtedly the jays. In North America, ornithologists studying the California Scrub Jay (*Aphelocoma californica*) have revealed its ability to recall the locations of more than 200 different caches, and for up to nine months after it hid them. Our Eurasian Jay is little different. The staple diet of this species is acorns, and over the course of a few weeks in autumn, when the crop peaks, one individual may cache up to 5,000 of the nuts. It may spend 10 hours per day completing this mammoth feat of labour, carrying up to nine acorns at a time in its sublingual pouch (see box, opposite). Jays bury their booty in natural holes and crevices, and under leaf litter. Then, over the course of winter, when food is short, they return to retrieve them, even digging them out from under 40cm (15in) of snow.

# The oak tree and the Jay

The Jay enjoys a unique symbiotic relationship with several species of oak. An oak releases most of its acorns between September and November. Jays collect many of them, generally selecting the healthy, good-sized ones, and bury them at a distance from the tree, from tens of metres to several kilometres away. They cache all the acorns carried in a single trip close to one another, but collectively these trips will cover a wide area. Research suggests that a group of 65 Jays may disperse up to 500,000 acorns in just four weeks.

A Jay generally buries its acorns in open areas with loose soil, usually along forest edges or in clearings, and covers each site with dirt and leaves. To locate the cache, it remembers the vertical structures of nearby vegetation. The buried acorns are retrieved throughout the year, but there is a drop-off from April to August when more insect food is available. This coincides with acorn germination, the seedling stem emerging during May and the first few leaves unfolding in June. By the time the seedling has emerged, Jays are helping their new young learn to forage. They will often pull up and eat an acorn, then drop the seedling back into the ground – but by now the seedling has developed taproots and can thus fend for itself, even if the acorn is removed. Research has shown that many oaks bear the scar of an early uprooting by a Jay, but this hasn't prevented them from developing into healthy trees.

This system benefits both parties. The oak receives ideal conditions in which to regenerate, with the Jay's selection strategy ensuring that only the strongest acorns have a good chance of germinating, and the tree's populations spread widely – including up hillsides, where any other form of dispersal would be impossible. The Jay, meanwhile, has a critical source of nutrition through leaner times. Closed forests are not suitable for the Jay, however, and it will not bury its acorns there. Thus, even though forest stands of oak produce 10 times more acorns than open-growth oak pasture landscapes, the density of acorns buried by Jays is 50 times greater within the latter. Such landscapes are generated by grazing, and while modern grazing has been created by humans, historically it would have been Wild Boar (*Sus scrofa*) that performed this service.

**Above:** A Jay searches for a suitable spot to cache an acorn.

# Crows at Home

The places where corvids live reflect their feeding and breeding requirements. Being such resourceful and versatile birds, most have plentiful options. Generalists such as Carrion Crows can live almost anywhere, while more specialised species such as Jays and Rooks require more particular habitats. Many have adapted well to the changes humankind has brought to the landscape, thriving where other birds have struggled. While most corvids are mainly sedentary, seldom travelling far beyond their breeding territories, a few make regular movements to find what they need.

## All over Britain

Worldwide, the Corvidae family occupies every known terrestrial biome except the polar ice caps, from Brown-necked Ravens in the barren Arabian Desert to Sri Lanka Blue Magpies in the steamy south Asian rainforests. In the UK, a small country with a temperate climate, each habitat is occupied by at least one species of corvid and most are home to several.

A quick glance at the distribution maps of our eight corvid species (see 'Meet the Crows') shows that nearly all range across most of the United Kingdom. The exceptions are the Chough, whose rarity and more specific habitat requirements confine it to just a few western locations, and the Hooded Crow, which is a northern counterpart of the Carrion Crow and occupies the same habitats. The area of the country with the lowest corvid density and variety is the far north-west of Scotland, where no species except the Hooded Crow and Raven inhabit the barest mountains and moorlands.

A big swathe of green across the map doesn't mean that the species in question occurs in every square kilometre, however. Within any particular region, most corvids gravitate towards specific habitats. Thus, in a

**Opposite:** Perched on rocks beside the Cornish coast, a Chough is in its element.

**Below:** Jackdaws have adapted well to built environments, exchanging cliffs for roofscapes.

typical area of hilly terrain, say in northern England or central Wales, you might find Ravens on the hilltops, Rooks in the fields below and Jays in the patches of woodland between the two. Some species, however – notably Carrion Crows, Hooded Crows, Jackdaws and Magpies – occur in almost every habitat type, with the exception of the deepest forests.

# Down on the farm

It is easy to forget that the open farmland typical of much of the UK – arable fields and livestock pastures neatly delineated by hedges and barbed wire, and punctuated with small stands of woodland – is a human creation. Our island was largely covered by forest until, sometime during the Neolithic period (10,000–4500 BC), the first farmers began felling the trees, starting a process that transformed our landscape from coast to coast. As the forests shrank, the tracts that remained came under increasing control and management, changing their ecology. Meanwhile, other 'unproductive' habitat types, such as wetlands, were lost to development over time.

For many forest species in ancient Britain, the arrival of agriculture began a process of decline; for some, including large mammals such as the Brown Bear (*Ursus arctos*) and Wild Boar, this spelt extinction. However, the new landscape offered opportunities for a range of birds, including Skylarks and Corn Buntings (*Emberiza calandra*), that were adapted to feeding in open grassland. Among these were corvids, most of which spend much of their life gleaning food from open ground. Today, Rooks, crows (both species), Jackdaws, Magpies and, in some areas, Ravens, are all common farmland birds, finding food in field and hedgerow, and nest sites in copse and village. What's more, while the intensification of modern farming has since caused a decline in many traditional farmland birds, including those same Skylarks and Corn Buntings, corvids have weathered these changes, their versatility allowing them to adapt to a more impoverished landscape.

**Below:** The Corn Bunting is typical of grassland specialists that have adapted to agricultural landscapes.

Of all the UK corvids, the most significant beneficiary of agriculture – and the most tied to farmland today – has been the Rook. This species is a grassland specialist, its bare face an adaptation to probing open ground. Scientists think it evolved far to the east, on the Asian steppes, and spread westward into Europe as people felled forests and opened up farmland – while leaving smaller stands of tall trees that served as rookeries and winter roosts. Today, the Rook remains the quintessential bird of farmland communities, its high-pitched *caw* still the soundtrack to every depiction of rural Britain, from *The Archers* to *This Country*. Believe it or not, there were no Rooks in the UK before farmers. Now, there are around 1 million pairs, with Britain and Ireland combined home to some 40 per cent of Europe's population.

With the success of reafforestation programmes elsewhere in Europe in recent years – for example, in Germany – Rook populations have fallen. Meanwhile, Mediterranean areas that appear to offer ideal open country are largely unpopulated by Rooks. The reason for this is that the birds' soil-probing habits require earth more softened by moisture than is available in the sun-baked southern summer – although some individuals do migrate south into Mediterranean regions during the rainier winter.

**Below:** Rooks and Jackdaws coexist productively in open farmland.

# Up in the hills

Rooks are low-altitude birds and do not generally breed above 300m (1,000ft). Higher up, other species prevail, notably Ravens. In the UK, these large corvids are emblematic of wild upland country, and are typically seen soaring around high crags in remote terrain. Here, they find undisturbed space for their large breeding territories, and can utilise the updraughts to soar widely in search of carrion and other food.

Uplands, however, are not the only place Ravens live. This species has one of the broadest habitat preferences of any bird, found from the Dead Sea to the Arctic tundra, and is described by Max Nicolson in the landmark *Birds of the Western Palearctic* (Vol. 8, 1994) as 'so wide-ranging that the concept of habitat is hardly applicable'. In the UK, the Raven's association with wild uplands reflects a history of persecution that saw the species eradicated from many of its traditional territories, including the Peak District, where it disappeared from 1863 until 1967. In recent years, protection has allowed Ravens to reclaim lost ground, and the species is increasingly found in lowland farmland and other habitats, returning to regions such as the south-east, where it was absent for decades. Today, the population stands at around 10,000 pairs, with central Wales thought to have one of the highest densities in Europe.

**Below left:** A Raven soars over typical wild uplands – though this species can adapt to many other habitats.

**Below right:** Jackdaws often form colonies on cliffs and in quarries.

Carrion Crows and, in Scotland, Hooded Crows also range widely through Britain's uplands, and both species may nest on the ground where there is insufficient tree cover. Jackdaws may also occur in hill country, and are particularly associated with cliffs and old quarries, where they find nest sites in rock crevices and ride the air currents around the precipices. The same is true of the Chough, which is largely an upland bird through much of its wider global range – although it is now rare in the UK and missing from most of its former upland haunts, the exception being Snowdonia. Magpies are not typical upland birds, but their versatility and ongoing population growth means they often venture to higher altitudes, provided there is enough nearby tree cover for nesting. Elsewhere in the world, notably in the Himalayas, Magpies have been recorded at impressive altitudes.

# Beside the water

Coasts provide a productive habitat for most corvids, and three of our species are particularly associated with them. Of these, Jackdaws are the most common and a noisy feature of many sea cliffs, where they nest in crevices – often near the likes of Fulmars (*Fulmarus glacialis*) and other seabirds – and ride the updraughts with aerobatic flair. Ravens also find nest sites on rock ledges, and are typically seen cruising along clifftops in pairs, betraying their presence with a telltale *cronk* and performing their rolling salute. They often find themselves in conflict with Peregrines, the two birds scrapping where their territories overlap.

Our third coastal corvid, and also the rarest, is the Chough. This species once ranged more widely, both around the coast and inland, but today is almost entirely confined to a handful of western clifftop locations, including in Cornwall, Wales, the Isle of Man and the Scottish island of Islay. The total UK population numbers 433 pairs (2014), with roughly 50 per cent in Wales and 30 per cent on the Isle of Man. Around double this number are found in Ireland, again mostly on the

**Below:** Ravens and Peregrines are traditional adversaries in clifftop habitats.

**Above:** A Chough flying over the sea in Pembrokeshire, South Wales.

**Below:** Hooded Crows gather to forage on a Scottish beach.

west coast. In England, the Chough is historically associated with Cornwall, where it features on the county coat of arms. By the 1920s, however, it had become rare even there – due, it is thought, to the decline of the tin-mining industry and thus the loss of the pit ponies that grazed the coastal pasture to precisely the length the Chough requires for foraging (see page 65). The last pair to nest in England during the 20th century was recorded in Cornwall in 1947. Since 2001, however, Choughs have been making a slow return to the county – aided by careful conservation (see page 125) – and in 2002, for the first time in more than 50 years, a pair raised young there.

Elsewhere, both Hooded and Carrion Crows often forage at the water's edge, on the coast and around inland wetlands, rivers and canals. They are quick to seize upon waste or carrion, and find numerous tasty titbits along the shoreline – whether worms and other invertebrates in the mud, or the unguarded eggs of ground-nesting waterbirds. Hooded Crows often work the strandline, rummaging through the seaweed, and are adept at opening shelled crabs and molluscs by flying up to drop them onto rocks below. Ravens may also gather at larger carcasses, such as those of seals and dolphins. In one record from Shetland, several hundred Ravens gathered to feed on the carcasses of beached Orcas (*Orcinus orca*).

# Deep in the woods

By and large, the UK's corvids avoid forests. Although crows, Rooks, Magpies and Jackdaws all nest in large trees, they still require surrounding mixed or open country in which to feed. These species may forage along woodland edges and in clearings, but they rarely venture into closed woodland. Indeed, the recent afforestation with large timber plantations of some areas, including in the Scottish Borders, Galloway and Northumberland, has led to local declines in the populations of Rooks and Ravens.

There is one exception to this rule. The Jay is decidedly a woodland bird, and never comfortable unless there are nearby trees into which it can beat a retreat. This reflects its staple diet: acorns. The distribution map (see page 29) thus shows that the Jay barely occurs north of Scotland's Great Glen and is largely absent from most of England's northern uplands. However, Jays don't need very large tracts of woodland, and in recent times they have shown a readiness to adapt to leafy suburbia.

**Below:** Jays are easily overlooked when foraging among woodland foliage, despite their bold colours.

# Corvids about town

The other significant way in which humans have altered the landscape for corvids – in addition to clearing forests – is through building. While towns, roads and factories have been disastrous for most wildlife, many corvids have bucked the trend by adapting readily to the built environment. Indeed, some have positively benefited from urbanisation.

In the UK today, several corvid species are among the commonest birds of our urban and suburban environments, finding plentiful food around streets, parks and rubbish dumps, and nest sites in buildings – occupied or abandoned. Moreover, by moving into town they avoid persecution they might otherwise suffer in the wider countryside. Carrion Crows in particular occur in virtually every urban and suburban environment and are a ubiquitous feature of any city park. Jackdaws are also at home in suburbia, finding nest sites in crevices and chimney pots, and are among the first corvids to occupy industrial sites after their closure. In the last half-century, Magpies have embraced town life: their UK population has quadrupled since the 1970s, with the highest rate of increase being in suburbia. And even Jays, once renowned as shy forest birds, are increasingly common in suburban gardens, especially in areas bordering woodland.

This embrace of our built environment has not been wholesale. London offers an interesting case study in the fortunes of urban corvids. Ravens, once common in the capital, have long since disappeared, leaving only their symbolic emissaries at the Tower of London (see page 119). Rooks also once thrived in the metropolis – there was once a rookery on Victoria Embankment – but as the city expanded, so their daily commute to out-of-town farmland became unsustainable and the population declined. Jackdaws, too, are now rare in central London, having once been common. Magpies, however, are more abundant than ever. And Jays, which were largely unknown in the capital until a pair

**Below:** A Magpie at home on a central London street – a rare sight just 50 years ago.

bred at Holland House in the 1920s, have steadily colonised the green spaces: first Battersea, then Hyde Park, Regent's Park and Kensington Gardens. Finally, by the end of the 20th century, this most colourful corvid had gone royal, breeding in the grounds of Buckingham Palace.

# Corvids on the move

**Above:** Rooks may commute between their roosting and feeding grounds in flocks many thousands strong.

Most British corvids are largely sedentary: in other words, they tend to spend their lives in and around the area in which they were raised. Young birds disperse from the immediate vicinity of their nest or colony during their first year, but seldom travel very far and often return to breed within cawing distance of their own home patch.

A 1960s study by ornithologist David Holyoak recorded the movements of large numbers of British corvids ringed and tracked over several years. Magpies emerged as the most confirmed homebodies, with only one in five recorded moving more than 8km (5 miles) from their nest, and only two individuals travelling more than 50km (32 miles). Jackdaws, by contrast, showed the greatest wanderlust, often travelling more than 160km (100 miles) during their first winter. The others fell somewhere in between, although among a few more adventurous individuals was a Raven that travelled 491km (305 miles) from Anglesey in Wales to East Lothian in Scotland.

During the course of a day, however, some corvids make significant movements. The best known are Rooks,

**Above:** Carrion Crows often gather in small flocks outside the breeding season, thus challenging the assumption that crows in a flock must be Rooks.

which commute every morning and evening between their rookery and the fields in which they feed. These movements become greater in winter when large flocks – sometimes many thousands strong – roost at a separate site, typically a dense wood, and may fly up to 45km (28 miles) each way. Indeed, these daily direct flights by Rooks from feeding ground to roost or breeding colony lie behind the expression 'as the crow flies'. Jackdaws often join Rooks in these mass commutes, their combined flocks producing an impressive spectacle as they stream back to their roost in the fading light.

Other corvids may also form larger roosts, especially outside the breeding season and during their first year, when juveniles gather in gangs after dispersing from their parents. Magpies and Carrion Crows may congregate in such gatherings, the latter thus challenging the folklore that a group of more than two crows together must be Rooks. Ravens also occasionally gather in surprising numbers: one historic roost in Newborough Warren, on Anglesey, has held up to 1,900 birds.

## Migrations and irruptions

The UK's corvids are not obligate migrants – in other words, none has evolved seasonal migration as a lifestyle strategy on which the species depends. Outside the UK, however, some do make more significant seasonal movements – especially populations that breed in more northerly or easterly climes, where harsh winters require them to head south or west in search of food. Rooks from Finland may move to wintering grounds in Denmark, for example, while those from eastern Europe may head for the Mediterranean, some travelling more than 2,500km (1,600 miles) in the process.

England once received a regular winter influx of Hooded Crows from northern and eastern Europe. These generally settled along the east coast, as far south as Kent, but some made it further inland. Indeed, the *Royston Crow*, a newspaper from Royston in Hertfordshire, features a Hooded Crow on its masthead – the legacy of a former age when the bird was a regular visitor to the county. Since the 1960s, however, this migration has steadily declined, with Hooded Crows now only rare winter visitors to the east coast of England.

The corvids most inclined to migrate are those that depend upon a single food supply that is subject to periodic shortages. Among UK corvids, this comes down to the acorn-eating Jay. While our resident Jay population is fairly sedentary, with birds moving little further than between nearby oak woods, we also receive a periodic winter influx of Jays from the Continent, forced west by the exhaustion of their oak crops or harsh winter conditions. Irregular migrations of this kind are called irruptions. Occasionally, exceptional numbers of Continental Jays arrive, distinguished from their local cousins by slightly different head markings. The years of 1957 and 1983 both witnessed such movements, with large numbers of Jays observed arriving off the North Sea along the east coast, and flocks flying west across the country. Such circumstances see some extraordinary records: in 1983, 1,500 Jays were counted flying over a garden in Land's End, Cornwall. Similar irruptions also explain the occasional visits of Nutcrackers to our shores (see page 31), driven west from the Siberian forests when their pine crops are exhausted.

**Below:** During autumn migration Jays may sometimes be seen passing overhead in small groups.

## Counting Rooks

The conspicuous nature of rookeries has long made the Rook one of the UK's easiest birds to census, with records going back centuries. Today, ornithologists can study historical patterns to understand long-term national population trends. The following data, published by A. Roebuck in *British Birds* magazine in June 1933, comes from a 1928–32 survey of Rooks in the English Midlands and gives a snapshot of population densities in that region nearly a century ago. Further data in the study – for example, the proportion of arable land in each county surveyed – helps provide a greater understanding of Rook populations on UK farmland.

| County | Area surveyed (sq miles) | No. of rookeries | Nests per rookery (average) | Total nests | Total breeding birds | Area (sq miles) per rookery (average) |
|---|---|---|---|---|---|---|
| Nottinghamshire | 843 | 182 | 35.7 | 6,501 | 13,002 | 4.6 |
| Leicestershire | 800 | 230 | 40.8 | 9,381 | 18,762 | 3.5 |
| Rutland | 152 | 49 | 47.7 | 2,340 | 4,680 | 3.1 |
| Derbyshire | 1,009 | 240 | 44.2 | 10,620 | 21,240 | 4.2 |
| Lincolnshire | 1,357 | 442 | 50.8 | 22,447 | 44,894 | 3 |
| **Total** | **4,161** | **1,143** | **44 (avg)** | **51,289** | **102,578** | **3.7 (avg)** |

# The Cycle of Life

The chief challenge for any corvid, as with all animals, is to usher more of its own kind into the world. To achieve this, all UK corvid species form strong pair-bonds in which both partners work closely to produce one brood a year. The work starts anew every spring, when the birds get together to build their nest, and continues until the fledglings venture out into the world two to three months later. It doesn't end there, however, as life is full of survival challenges that every young corvid must negotiate if it is to fulfil its breeding potential.

# Breeding

Every year, as spring approaches, corvids turn their attention to breeding. Most UK corvid species tend not to breed until their third year, although Magpies may breed during year two. For most, the process is underway by mid- to late March. Ravens may start as early as February, although in more northerly regions they may delay breeding until late April, and Hooded Crows in Shetland may not be on the nest until mid-May.

Breeding behaviour is triggered by hormonal changes within a bird as it responds to changing day length. These internal triggers are powerful. In her book *Corvus: A Life with Birds*, Esther Woolfson describes how her hand-reared female Rook named Chicken, which had never ventured outside, let alone met another of her own kind, entered a frenzy of breeding behaviour for a few weeks every spring, collecting and shredding newspaper to build her own nest under the kitchen table, clattering her food dishes and pulling out wires, while displaying and calling insistently. 'I'm moved by the steadfastness she displays,' writes Woolfson, 'saddened by knowing that she is dedicated to a task that can have no positive conclusion.'

**Opposite:** A female Carrion Crow broods her chicks on a treetop nest in Wales.

# Finding a place

The first challenge of breeding is to secure a safe place with sufficient resources in which to go about it; in other words, a territory. Territory size varies by species. A pair of Carrion Crows generally requires anything from $0.1km^2$ (0.04 sq miles) to $1km^2$ (0.39 sq miles), depending on the local population density, while a pair of Ravens in remote country might claim up to $25km^2$ (9.65 sq miles) or more. Others, such as Rooks, Jackdaws and Choughs, live more communally, each pair holding a small territory within a larger one occupied by the group. Either way, most corvids show strong site fidelity, a pair often returning to nest in the same place, or close by, year after year. Some, including Magpies, remain on these territories year-round. Others, including Carrion Crows, may move away outside the breeding season but return in time to breed in early spring.

Rooks are among the best-studied examples of communal living in the bird world, breeding in close-knit communities called rookeries that comprise tens and sometimes hundreds of pairs – one Rook colony in Aberdeenshire numbered more than 1,000 pairs. The constant noisy comings and goings make these arguably the most conspicuous breeding colonies of any UK bird.

**Right:** Ravens choose remote, inaccessible nest sites with a large surrounding territory.

Inside a rookery, each pair's nest forms a microhabitat, which it defends from others – as with those of seabirds such as Gannets (*Morus bassanus*). Jackdaw and Chough colonies are smaller and looser, but nonetheless benefit from the same principle of safety in numbers, in which all pairs nest in sight of their neighbours and can thus jump to the colony's collective defence.

**Above:** Rooks are the most communal breeders of UK corvids, nesting in large treetop colonies called rookeries.

## Pairing up

In spring, a breeding pair must first get together. All UK corvid species form strong monogamous pair-bonds that often last for life. However, even long-established pairs must go through their annual courtship rituals, while first-timers must hook up with a new mate. In both cases, this involves a courtship display, in which the male aims to impress the female by demonstrating his agility, attentiveness, intelligence, resourcefulness and other must-have qualities in a corvid mate.

Rooks in a rookery provide an easy-to-observe example of corvid courtship rituals. An established pair renew their bonds on or beside the nest. The male generally gets things started, bowing with drooping wings and raising his fanned tail. The female responds by crouching, arching her back and quivering her wings in a submissive begging posture – the male often meeting these demands by presenting a gift of food, this sometimes triggering a playful tug of war.

Colour also helps. Magpies and Jays deploy their bold markings, raising and lowering their head feathers, and lifting

**Above:** A male Rook (right) lowers his wings and raises his tail as part of a courtship display to his mate.

and fanning their tails. A male Magpie spreads its white shoulder-patches, while a Jay flaunts its brilliant blue wing-coverts. Even 'all-black' corvids such as the Carrion Crow and Rook can flaunt a dazzling, iridescent spectrum of blues, greens and violets. These birds' capacity to detect ultraviolet light means that they perceive far more colour in each other's plumage than is visible to our more limited sight.

First-timers are the most vigorous in their courtship performance, looking to outcompete the opposition in daring aerobatic displays. Young Rooks, Jackdaws and Choughs plummet down from on high, wings folded, while Ravens perform their signature rolls, flipping over onto their back or corkscrewing briefly downwards, and Magpies pursue each other in buoyant chases, wings and tails fanned.

Once a pair is established, partners reinforce their bonds by allogrooming, fluffing up their head and nape feathers as an invitation to preen, and regularly fondling bills. They also duet together – not with the usual harsh tones, but using softer, sweeter notes. These displays continue beyond the breeding season: a pair of Ravens, in particular, remain very close, travelling together all year and often performing their aerobatics. Watch a feeding or flying flock of Jackdaws and you'll soon see that pairs stick together, even in the crowd. Indeed, studies of Jackdaw colonies have shown that pairs benefit from a shared status within their group, a new mate acquiring its partner's higher rank.

Copulation usually takes place on or near the nest, the female inviting the male's approach by crouching and raising her tail. In rookeries, this action may precipitate a rumpus, with neighbouring birds mobbing the mating pair and alien males even trying to mate if they find themselves on top of the female. Indeed, despite the strength of the monogamous pair-bond, extra-pair copulations are not uncommon in corvids as opportunist males seek out other females to spread their genetic legacy a little further.

**Above left:** A pair of Jackdaws engage in allogrooming to cement their pair bond.

**Above right:** A pair of courting Magpies typically chase each other from perch to perch.

## Choosing a nest site

Most corvid species nest primarily in trees – typically mature ones with plentiful greenery. Rooks generally site their rookeries in a stand of Elms (*Ulmus minor*), Ashes (*Fraxinus excelsior*), beeches or other tall deciduous trees. These become highly conspicuous in winter, once the leaves have fallen, as do the individual nests of crows and Magpies, whose bulky structures are also typically located high up. Magpies and Jays may sometimes also nest a little lower, in dense hedges and shrubs. In remote areas, where suitable trees are unavailable, both Carrion Crows and Hooded Crows may occasionally nest on the ground.

Jackdaws are primarily crevice nesters. They tend to choose more sheltered sites than Rooks, and often take over tree holes from other birds such as Great Spotted Woodpeckers (*Dendrocopos major*) and Stock Doves

**Above:** Noisy activity around rookeries draws attention to the birds' nests in the treetops.

(*Columba oenas*). Away from trees, colonies use the cracks and crevices of cliffs and quarries, and old buildings – from battlements and belfries to chimney pots on terraced houses. It seems this affinity for buildings is nothing new: in his celebrated *The Natural History and Antiquities of Selborne* (1789), the naturalist Gilbert White (1720–93) records Jackdaws nesting under the lintels of Stonehenge.

Carrion Crows and Hooded Crows will also nest in buildings, and sometimes use pylons and utility poles – as, on occasion, do Ravens. Crows and Magpies often choose sites close to roads, aiming to benefit from a plentiful supply of roadkill, and Magpie nests are often conspicuous in tall trees along the verges. Ravens prefer places away from disturbance and, although they sometimes nest in trees, they often prefer rocky ledges on crags and sea cliffs, where they construct an eagle-like eyrie.

**Below left:** Suburban Jackdaws often nest in chimney pots.

**Below right:** Choughs site their nest in a hidden crevice or cave.

Jackdaws are also cliff nesters, establishing small colonies on sea cliffs and inland quarries, where individual pairs each find a suitable crevice. Choughs do likewise, using caves, quarries and sometimes old mine shafts. Elsewhere in the world, Choughs also nest alongside people – including in working monasteries in Tibet and even on modern buildings in Mongolia.

## Construction work

With the location chosen, the pair must build their nest. This is a shared task, the male generally gathering most of the material while the female focuses on construction. The majority of nests comprise a large mass of bulky twigs – plucked from trees to the correct size – that encloses a deep central cup sealed with mud or clay and lined with softer material, such as grass, moss, roots and bark. Each species has its own variations on this theme. Jackdaws and Choughs often use sheep's wool as a lining, while Jays may supplement this with feathers and Ravens with deer fur. In coastal regions, Hooded Crows incorporate seaweed into the structure, and often bones and wire. Rooks are not above stealing material from the nests of their neighbours.

The largest individual corvid nests are those of Ravens, which have been measured at up to 153cm (60in) wide by 61cm (24in) deep. Rooks occasionally make compound nests, however, which may house up to eight pairs and measure around 1m by 2m (3ft by 6.5ft). Jackdaws may also create massive structures, albeit inadvertently, by continuing to drop sticks down a chimney into a cavity that

**Below left:** A Jackdaw carries a hazel twig, cropped to a precise length for its chimney pot nest.

**Below right:** Magpie nests are large and conspicuous.

is deeper than they realise. Such nests may block chimneys, and sometimes crash down into the fireplace below, often carrying with them their cargo of eggs or chicks.

Size apart, the most impressive nest must be that of the Magpie. This bulky stick structure, built in a tree fork, is cemented with earth and clay and roofed with a dome of prickly branches, leaving a small, concealed entrance through which the parents come and go. It has long been said that Magpies also go a stage further, decorating their nest with shiny objects they have 'stolen' from people or households (see page 118). However, no studies have been able to establish whether this reputation has any basis in fact.

## Eggs and incubation

Corvids lay 3–7 eggs, with 4–6 being a typical clutch size for most species. Magpies may exceptionally lay up to 10. The eggs are green to greenish blue, overlaid with a variable patterning of grey and brownish blotches. Jackdaw eggs are a little lighter and those of the Chough creamier in colour.

The female typically lays her eggs early in the morning, producing one per day over several days. In most species, she alone is largely responsible for incubation, using the brood-patch of soft skin on her belly to keep the clutch warm, although male Jays may also take their turn on the eggs. Through this period, the male's main job is to bring

**Below:** A female Hooded Crow settles down to incubate her eggs.

| Corvid incubation and fledging periods | | | |
|---|---|---|---|
| Species | Incubation (days) | Fledging (days) | Total (days) |
| Jay | 16–19 | 20–23 | 42 |
| Carrion Crow | 17–20 | 28–30 | 50 |
| Magpie | 21–22 | 22–28 | 50 |
| Rook | 16–18 | 32–33 | 51 |
| Jackdaw | 17–18 | 28–35 | 53 |
| Hooded Crow | 17–19 | 32–36 | 55 |
| Chough | 17–18 | 31–41 | 59 |
| Raven | 18–21 | 35–42 | 63 |

food to his mate. Incubation lasts roughly 2–3 weeks, ranging from as little as 16 days in some Rooks and Jays to as long as 22 days in some Magpies. Once the chick is ready to hatch, it uses its egg tooth – a small projection on the upper mandible of its bill, lost soon after hatching – to chip through the shell and clamber into the outside world.

## Fledging

Corvid chicks are altricial, which means that they hatch from the egg blind, naked and helpless. The rate at which they subsequently fledge varies with the species and conditions, but ranges from as little as 20 days after hatching in Jays to as long as 42 days in Ravens. In Magpies, the chicks' eyes open at around day seven; by day eight, their body is covered in down and by day 10, their primary wing feathers have emerged.

For a week to 10 days after the eggs hatch, a female corvid broods her clutch while the male brings food – typically first passing it to his partner, which then offers it to the voracious chicks. Thereafter, both parents share feeding duties: 10 days after her clutch has hatched, a female Rook will have joined her partner to forage for them, making regular flights to the surrounding fields and returning each time with her sublingual pouch bulging with goodies.

**Below:** An adult Raven delivers food to its young in the nest.

**Above:** A Jay mobs a roosting Tawny Owl, which poses a potential threat to its young.

A few corvids around the world are cooperative breeders. This means that the breeding pair's offspring from the previous season postpone their own breeding cycle to help their parents raise the new brood. In the USA, the Florida Scrub Jay provides one well-documented example of this unusual behaviour. However, a small proportion of Carrion Crows are also known to do the same, especially in barren environments.

Corvids can be very aggressive in defence of their nest, the male and female working together to drive away intruders, which may include other corvids as well as predatory mammals such as Stoats (*Mustela erminea*) and domestic cats. Carrion Crows will attack dogs and cats, and pairs from adjacent territories may join forces against a common threat such as a raptor. In Sweden, Jackdaws have been seen driving off predators as large as Pine Martens (*Martes martes*), and Ravens are known to drop stones on unwanted visitors. When a brooding Jay detects an approaching predator, its first defence is to vacate the nest discreetly, then give a loud alarm call to distract attention. If the predator is already too close, however, it will spread its wings and gape threateningly. Finally, if all else fails, it will fly at the intruder, attacking with bill and feet, while giving raucous alarm calls – both its own and those of the intruder.

As young corvids approach their fledging date they become increasingly restless, flapping their wings and often leaving the nest to clamber around in nearby branches. Soon they take their first flight – inept initially, but improving as they gain strength and experience. However, they are not independent yet. For another 4–6 weeks, the youngsters will hang around the nest, where their parents continue to feed and protect them from predators. In Ravens, this period may extend to six months, the youngsters continuing to learn new foraging tricks from their experienced parents. And in Carrion Crows, the youngsters may remain with their parents for a year or more if they serve as 'helpers' (see above).

## Growing up

By midsummer, with breeding over, the countryside is full of newly fledged corvids learning the ropes. They are generally not hard to distinguish from adults. In the largely black species (Raven, Rook, Carrion Crow, Hooded Crow, Jackdaw and Chough), the plumage lacks the sleek, glossy adult iridescence and instead is suffused with duller brownish tones. Pale patches in the wings show in flight, and the bill is shorter and at the base may show the remains of the fleshy gape. There are also a few other more specific clues: juvenile Rooks lack the adults' whitish facial skin (but can still be distinguished from Carrion Crows by their peaked forehead and pointier bill), juvenile Choughs have a bill that is yellowish brown rather than bright red, and juvenile Magpies have a much shorter, stubbier tail than adults. Young Jays have no specific juvenile markings but resemble a scruffier version of the adult.

Life is hard for young corvids. Before a brood even fledges, some chicks will already have perished as nestlings. These are usually the youngest: they started life at a disadvantage due to the staggered hatching of the eggs, which left them the smallest and weakest when competing with their siblings for limited food in the nest. And then, for all their intelligence and resourcefulness, at least half the fledged brood of most species will not survive their first year. In one study of Magpies in Sheffield, only 22 per cent made it through year one, although 69 per cent of these went on to survive beyond year two.

To boost their chances of survival, young corvids form flocks, often spending their first winter in adolescent gangs that roost and feed together. It is at this time that you may encounter otherwise non-social species, such as Carrion Crows, Magpies and Ravens, in surprisingly large groups. If they survive their first winter, these youngsters will have become wiser and tougher, and will greet the next spring as young adults ready to take their first tentative steps in the mating game. With the exception of Magpies, however, breeding success for most corvids does not generally come until the following year or, in Ravens, even the year after that.

The failure rate among young corvids may seem wasteful, even cruel, but it reflects an insurance policy built into the breeding strategy. As with other passerines, a pair of corvids produces more eggs than they need. In extremely good years, the whole clutch might make it – but in order to replace their parents and thus maintain a stable population,

**Above:** A young Carrion Crow shows paler, less glossy plumage than an adult.

**Below:** A young Magpie has a shorter tail than an adult.

**Right:** After fledging, young Magpies band together in small groups to explore their new world.

only two need to make it to full breeding adulthood. The others – victims of disease, starvation or predators – form what are known to scientists as the 'sustainable surplus'. It is rare for UK corvids to attempt more than one brood a year, although Rooks have been known to try for a second time if their first breeding attempt fails completely.

# Staying alive

If a young corvid survives its first year then, with a little luck, it may lead a full and productive life. But even mature adults face plenty of challenges, from dodging predators to avoiding accidents, finding food, and simply keeping fit and healthy. The time of highest mortality is the early breeding season when birds are working around the clock to defend a territory and feed a voracious brood, and under such intense pressure are thus more vulnerable to attack, accident or disease. Most take these challenges in their stride, however, and some go on to reach impressive ages (see page 99).

## Keeping fit and healthy

Health challenges for corvids begin in the nest, where fleas, mites and other parasites may afflict chicks. Parents pay close attention to nest hygiene, removing their chicks' droppings in the form of faecal sacs, which they either eat or jettison away from the nest, until the youngsters can clamber onto the nest rim and defecate over the side.

Adult corvids are also susceptible to disease, their scavenging habits making them more vulnerable than many passerines. Studies show that Carrion Crows, Magpies and Jays (and thus, presumably, other corvid species) host various haemosporidian (blood) parasites that are carried by mosquitoes; one study of Ravens in Bulgaria showed that 49 per cent were affected. These parasites cause diseases such as avian malaria, although many birds can sustain the parasite load and remain reasonably healthy. In 1999, the American Crow was found to be a major carrier of the West Nile virus in the USA, which may also afflict humans.

A bird's fitness also depends upon keeping its plumage in tip-top condition. Feathers suffer considerable wear and tear, so corvids preen regularly to remove dirt, parasites and damaged feathers. They use their bill to manipulate the feathers individually, anointing each with oil from the uropygial (preen) gland at the base of the tail for lubrication. Corvids get some preening assistance from their companions, which will concentrate on the tricky head and nape areas that a bird can't reach with its own bill. This 'allogrooming' also serves important social functions between mates and companions (see page 88).

Corvids bathe regularly, both by perching in the rain or, especially during the hot summer months, by wading into a shallow pool such as a bird bath and ducking down to splash the water over their plumage. They may also sunbathe, finding a warm sunlit spot in which to fluff out their plumage and spread their wings to distribute the preen oil through their feathers and drive out parasites.

On top of these maintenance routines, corvids also undergo one complete annual moult, replacing their worn feathers with a new set. In this respect, they are unusual among passerines, most of which moult twice a year. The process begins just after breeding and takes 3–4 months to complete – from 92 days in Choughs to 140 days in Ravens. The primary wing feathers are replaced first, ensuring that the bird can fly while the rest of its plumage is upgraded.

**Below:** Jays are regular visitors to bird baths and woodland pools.

# Ant antics

Most UK corvids occasionally practise a strange-looking ritual known as 'anting', in which they perch on or near an ants' nest and allow the angry insects to swarm through their plumage. This behaviour has been recorded in 10 bird species in the UK. The formic acid secreted by the ants in self-defence is thought to act as an insecticide, helping to clear mites and other parasites from the birds' plumage and ridding it of harmful bacteria. The Jay is the best-known exponent of anting. Typically, it will land on top of a Southern Wood Ant (*Formica rufa*) nest, spread its wings forwards, tuck its tail down and enter a kind of convulsive shuddering as the insects get to work, shaking its head to remove any that climb too high. This technique is known as 'passive anting'. Some birds, including the Magpie, also practise 'active anting', whereby

**Above:** An anting Jay contorts its body to allow the insects access to its plumage.

they grasp the insects in their bill and insert them more precisely among their feathers. Jackdaws have been recorded perching in chimney smoke, and it is thought they may be deliberately fumigating their plumage for similar purposes.

# Avoiding danger

However fit and healthy an adult corvid may be, it still faces numerous hazards. These include accidents. Corvids are sometimes injured or killed in collisions with human-made objects such as buildings or power lines. Many are also struck by vehicles as they scavenge on road verges – although drivers often marvel at the birds' canny ability to get out of the way at the last second.

A more pressing concern for most corvids is keeping out of the clutches of predators. The danger starts in the nest, where chicks or eggs may be targeted by arboreal predators such as Pine Martens or even other corvids. Parents will attack vigorously to thwart any would-be nest raider, but their efforts may be in vain when they themselves are on the menu. In this respect, raptors present the greatest threat. Magpies, Jays and Jackdaws are all fair game for a female Sparrowhawk (*Accipiter nisus*) and are often taken. The larger Peregrine will also take these species and sometimes even Hooded and Carrion Crows. The Goshawk (*A. gentilis*) is a rare bird in the UK but regularly predates all corvids elsewhere in Europe, including Ravens. And Ravens, despite

**Below:** A Carrion Crow drives away a Buzzard from its breeding territory.

being formidable predators in their own right, may fall prey to the Golden Eagle and White-tailed Eagle (*Haliaeetus albicilla*) in the Scottish Highlands, where these two huge predators also regularly predate Hooded Crows.

Corvids are no pushover for a predator. They are fast and agile in flight, able to evade an attack if they see it coming – a quick search of home videos on YouTube reveals how bravely a Magpie will fight to escape a Sparrowhawk that has it pinioned to the ground. In these circumstances, the victim's companions may gather to mob the predator in an attempt to disrupt its attack.

Prevention is better than cure, however, which is why corvids are quick to take to the air and drive a passing raptor out of their territory. It also explains the raucous calls with which they sound the alarm, a screeching Jay informing all that there's a Sparrowhawk in the wood, or a chattering suburban Magpie blowing the cover of a prowling cat. Corvids captured by predators are most often young birds that haven't yet learned how to keep out of harm's way.

One predator, however, presents a more inexorable threat: our own species has long taken a heavy toll on corvids. Today, it remains legal to kill Carrion Crows, Hooded Crows, Rooks, Jackdaws, Jays and Magpies under a general licence (see page 120). Any of these birds can be shot – or trapped in a legal Larsen trap and then humanely destroyed – if deemed to be a pest. Only Ravens and Choughs, the latter rare in the UK, are exempt. This explains why in many rural situations corvids have learned to be very wary of a human with a gun.

**Above:** A Magpie struggles in vain to escape the lethal talons of a Sparrowhawk.

# A ripe old age?

Most corvids live an average of 5–10 years in the wild. If they get lucky, however, they may last twice as long. In UK ringing studies, Jays, Carrion Crows and Hooded Crows have been recorded at over 17 years, Jackdaws at over 18 years, Choughs at over 20 years, Ravens and Magpies at over 21 years, and Rooks at 22 years. This is considerably longer than most other passerines. However, it may represent only a fraction of their potential, as some captive corvids have lived far beyond this – most notably a Raven that reached an astonishing 69 years old.

**Below:** Road traffic is an occupational hazard to corvids that scavenge along the verge.

# Intelligence and Communication

Corvids have long divided opinion. Where some admire their resourcefulness, others revile them as destructive or malevolent. Few, however, disagree that these birds appear to be unusually intelligent – and science now confirms this perception to be more than folklore. These birds, it turns out, are not only the cleverest members of the avian world, perhaps even surpassing their brainy rivals the parrots, but they have cognitive powers rivalling those of the great apes and second only to our own. The roots of this intelligence lie in the birds' social behaviour and are today the subject of fascinating research.

## Intelligence

'If men had wings and black feathers, few of them would be clever enough to be crows.' The words of celebrated 19th-century American clergyman and abolitionist Henry Ward Beecher (1813–87) were prescient, given what we now know about corvids. These birds have a brain-to-body-mass ratio on par with that of Chimpanzees (*Pan troglodytes*) and their behaviour exhibits comparable mental faculties. In some tests, crows have outperformed a seven-year-old child.

Corvid intelligence embraces causal reasoning, an ability to use and even fashion tools, a prodigious memory, self-awareness and empathy with companions. Many species have also revealed a capacity for play and an apparent ability to express emotions such as grief. Happily, you needn't be a scientist working in a laboratory to observe the corvid brain in action: pay close attention to our UK species in their everyday environment, and you may be surprised by what they get up to.

**Opposite:** A Rook uses both bill and brain as it works out how to get into a rubbish bin.

**Right:** A Raven participates in a research experiment at the Konrad Lorenz Institute in Austria.

## Tactics and tools

Corvids can improvise highly innovative ways of finding food. Ravens, for example, will pull up a line from a fishing hole and steal the catch on the end. Hooded Crows will drop clams onto rocks from the air to crack open the contents. Rooks will work together to haul up the lining of an outdoor rubbish bin – securing it with their feet, pleat by pleat – to access the food at the bottom. And Carrion Crows in one Japanese city have even learned to place walnuts in front of the wheels of cars stopped at traffic lights, flying down after the lights have changed and the cars have driven over the nuts to retrieve the contents from the cracked shells.

Such examples show causal reasoning: an ability to manipulate the environment to achieve predicted outcomes. They do not in themselves demonstrate tool use, which scientists define as using one object as an extension of the body to manipulate another. However, corvids can do this, too. In the US, the American Crow and Green Jay have been seen using twigs to prise insects from crevices, while scientists have observed Carrion Crows in the Middle East using pieces of wire mesh to scoop up and filter food they've cached beneath the sand. In captivity, Magpies may use twigs to clean their cage and Carrion Crows employ pieces of wire to retrieve food.

The most celebrated tool user among the world's corvids is undoubtedly the New Caledonian Crow. This South Pacific species takes things a step further by manufacturing its own tools. It does this both by pruning twigs to size for poking into crevices, and by tearing strips from the barbed leaves of *Pandanus* plants and trimming them into a hook with which to winkle out insect larvae. Experiments with New Caledonian Crows have shown that they can use a selection of different tools in sequence to solve complex challenges. These include selecting the correct length of stick to secure an out-of-reach object and dropping stones into water to raise its level and thus reach a prize floating on top.

**Above:** A New Caledonian Crow uses a stick to prise food from bark crevices.

## Never forget

Corvids demonstrate an impressive memory. This is especially evident in Jays, which are able to retrieve thousands of acorns cached in multiple scattered locations over many months (see page 71). Studies of the California Scrub Jay show that these birds retrieve perishable food items before others, thus remembering not only where they cached their supplies but also when. This suggests that the birds have an episodic memory – an ability, once thought unique to humans, to recall the precise time and place of past experiences.

Corvids' powerful memory allows them to learn quickly from experience. Renowned corvid expert John Marzluff at the University of Washington, USA, conducted a long-term study of American Crows in which researchers who trapped the birds wore a special 'danger' face mask (modelled on then Vice President Dick Cheney). When other people subsequently wore the same mask, even when walking harmlessly across campus, they were loudly scolded by the birds, which recognised it. What's more, the number of birds doing the scolding increased with time, which means that they were passing on the knowledge to companions that had never themselves suffered the trauma of capture.

**Above:** Rooks on an urban street quickly learn exactly where and when to find the most productive scavenging.

Such studies help explain the speed with which corvids learn to be wary of, say, a farmer with a shotgun. These birds have adapted to live alongside us and, in the process, have learned to observe us closely. The crows or Magpies in your suburban neighbourhood will know who puts the rubbish out and where, which children throw stones or discard snacks, which car belongs to which house, and so on. No threat or opportunity escapes their quick-thinking, beady-eyed vigilance.

## Fun and games

One of the more intriguing aspects of corvid behaviour is the birds' propensity for what scientists call 'unrewarded object exploration' – or what others might describe as simply having fun. Many species have been observed

**Below:** Rooks on a snowy roof contemplate a spot of tobogganing – perhaps.

doing things that have no evident survival value, seemingly for the sheer pleasure of it. Examples are legion: Hooded Crows tobogganing down a snow-covered roof on a plastic lid, then carrying the lid back to the top to repeat the process, again and again; and Carrion Crows flying over a cooling tower, where they can take a free ride up on a column of heated air and then parachute back down again. Author Esther Woolfson describes how her pet Magpie Spike would deliberately balance a matchbox on top of a door frame, seemingly for the joy of seeing it drop to the ground when the

door was opened, and would leave coffee cups teetering on a table's edge, apparently for the same thrill – and with disastrous consequences for the family crockery.

Many corvids seem to get a special kick from taunting other animals. Ravens will creep up close behind a large predator in an apparent game of 'catch me if you can', flying away when it turns on them and then returning to repeat the process. Pet owners who have reared corvids testify to the merciless way in which these birds pull the tails of cats and dogs. One amateur video clip from Russia shows a Hooded Crow goading two cats into a scrap. With the animals already in a stand-off, the bird flits between them, calling loudly, pecking at their tails and working them into a fever pitch. When the cats finally fly at each other, the bird hops around them like a referee in a boxing bout, continuing to squawk in apparent excitement at the spectacle.

It is hard to know how corvids benefit from behaviour of this kind. Marzluff points out that endorphins – pleasure-related chemicals – feel good in corvids just as they do in humans. But what is the evolutionary point of pleasure? Play in animals is generally explained as a means of developing vital survival skills; only in humans is pleasure from recreational activity seen as an end in itself. The more we know about corvids, however, the more these distinctions seem to blur.

**Left:** The Indian House Crow, like many corvids, appears to enjoy provoking a reaction from cats and other larger animals.

# Social skills

Fossil evidence reveals that corvid ancestors were sociable birds and today, to a greater or lesser extent, all our species have social lives. Some, such as Rooks and Jackdaws, spend all their time in large communities. Others, including Ravens and Carrion Crows, group together at certain times, such as on their non-breeding roosts and at a large common food source.

Communal living has its pros and cons. A strong community can mount an effective collective defence against predators – especially during the breeding season when even solitary breeders such as Carrion Crows will waive territorial rivalries in a joint show of force against a raptor. Birds in a community can also share information about food sources: Rooks at a rookery will observe when their neighbours return in the evening with a crop full of food and will make sure to follow them the next day to wherever they found it. Thus, birds living together can teach one another, whether deliberately or otherwise. These lessons pass down through generations.

Life in a community also brings challenges, however, with individuals competing for food and nest sites. Highly sociable species such as Jackdaws and Rooks

**Below:** Large communal roosts serve as information centres for corvids such as these Rooks.

establish linear dominance hierarchies, within which each individual must solve social problems to acquire and maintain status and thus secure resources for itself. To negotiate the challenges and politics of communal living, corvids have evolved impressive communication skills and a closer understanding of their companions.

**Above:** Carrion Crows from different territories may band together to drive away raptors, such as this Red Kite (*Milvus milvus*).

## Communication

Corvids are not generally celebrated for their voices. After all, their harsh calls – the *caw* of a Rook, croak of a Raven or rattle of a Magpie – are hardly a match for the melodious strains of passerines such as, say, a Blackbird. However, corvids are among the most articulate of birds. In communicating with one another – to convey alarm, partnership, information and other social functions – they produce a multiplicity of sounds, some so soft and subtle that they often escape human ears.

Many corvids are accomplished mimics. Jays imitate other birds in their woodland home with uncanny accuracy, including predators such as the Buzzard and Goshawk. They have even been known to mimic a Tawny Owl to scare Carrion Crows from their nest. Ravens can do a good rendition of inanimate sounds, from car engines to flushing toilets, and human speech presents little problem: the individuals at the Tower of London

**Above:** Magpies reared by hand make entertaining and challenging pets.

(see page 119) will call 'Keep the path!' to straying visitors. Hand-reared Jackdaws or Magpies quickly learn greetings and commands. Spike, Esther Woolfson's tame Magpie, had a vocabulary that included 'What?', 'Oy!' and 'Hello Spikey'. He would even say 'Hello' down a telephone to a disembodied voice at the other end.

Body language provides an additional lexicon. Such codified gestures as fluffing up the nape, fanning the tail or crouching down with bill raised all convey messages between birds – sometimes to establish dominance or submission to avoid conflict, and at other times to reaffirm bonds between companions or partners. Jackdaws form selective partnerships from an early age, often of the same sex, and body language helps maintain these. Partners support each other with allogrooming (see page 88) and bill-twining, and will even seek solace in the other's company after a bust-up with a third party. Many games that young corvids play, from 'king of the mountain' to 'follow the leader', serve to sort out hierarchies and partnerships.

## Knowing yourself and understanding others

In 2008, a captive Magpie became the first bird to pass a mirror test. This exercise entailed marking the bird's throat feathers with small dots that it was unable to see, then revealing to the bird its reflected image in a mirror. The Magpie, recognising the image as itself, immediately attempted to remove the spots from its feathers. This apparently simple test revealed something very unusual in the animal kingdom: self-awareness. The Magpie showed that it was aware of its own identity as an individual. Other than ourselves, only great apes, bottlenose dolphins (*Tursiops* species) and the Asian Elephant (*Elephas maximus*) have been shown to have this awareness.

If you are aware of yourself as an individual, it follows that you must also be aware that other individuals are different. This paves the way for what scientists call 'theory of mind': the idea that other individuals may have desires,

**Below:** The Asian Elephant has demonstrated a capacity for self-awareness comparable to that of a Magpie.

intentions and perspectives that are different from our own – and, in turn, empathy, or the ability to recognise and understand the states of mind of others. Theory of mind was once thought unique to humans: a key quality that distinguishes us from the rest of the animal kingdom. In recent years, however, it has been revealed as a critical part of the social interactions of great apes – and, now, corvids.

Studies have shown how Ravens, Jays and other corvids know when they're being spied upon while caching food. If they suspect the spy to be a thief, they employ various tactics to throw it off the scent – either using a barrier to screen their caching (thus demonstrating they can imagine what the thief can and can't see), or by making a public show of their activity and then returning after the intruder has departed to remove the food and relocate it. However, individual birds will practise this subterfuge only if they themselves are thieves and if they know the other individual to be one too. Indeed, a Jay will hide its cache only if the bird observing it is socially dominant. In the world of corvid caching, it takes one to know one.

**Above:** The California Scrub Jay will deceive potential thieves by making a public display of caching food before returning secretly to remove and relocate it.

Empathy among corvids runs further than just suspicion. Individuals will also actively console partners or companions that have come off worst in a fight. This raises another contentious issue: can corvids experience and express emotion? Numerous observations report Carrion Crows, Magpies and others paying unusual attention to a dead companion – gathering around the fallen bird, uttering strange cries and even laying pieces of vegetation beside it, like funeral wreaths. It is impossible to say whether these birds feel grief as we understand it, but nonetheless they appear to be confronting the death of one of their own in a deliberate and ritualised way. Perhaps it is a 'teachable' moment, in which the circumstances of their companion's death helps them learn valuable lessons for their own future.

# What's in a brain?

Corvids certainly have the brains to explain their braininess. These organs are relatively larger than those of any other bird except parrots: a Raven's brain, for example, weighs about 1.3 per cent of its body mass – about the same as in great apes. A corvid's brain is very different in structure from that of an ape, however, or indeed of any mammal. While mammalian brains are layered, producing a wrinkled appearance, avian brains are nucleated, consisting of different areas, each with its own function. Thus, birds do not have a prefrontal cortex – the area of the forebrain responsible for most cognitive activity in mammals. Instead, they have an area known as the nidopallium caudolaterale, which is densely packed with neurons and does roughly the same job. The nidopallium in corvids is comparatively as large as the prefrontal cortex in Chimpanzees; in a Raven, it accounts for 80 per cent of the whole brain mass.

**Right:** The brain of a Chimpanzee and a corvid are similar in relative size, though they differ in structure.

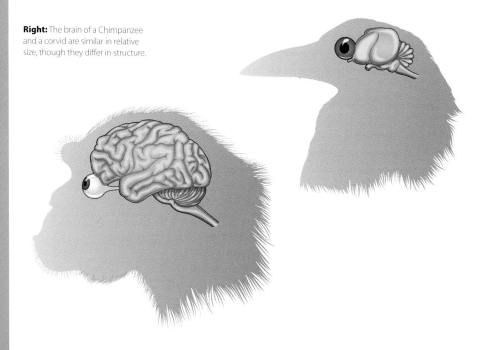

It is not surprising that the brains of birds and mammals are so physically different, given that their evolutionary paths diverted some 300 million years ago. What intrigues scientists, however, is that corvid brains should function in such a similar way to those of great apes. And this is not because corvids are the most evolutionarily 'advanced' of birds, as was once thought: we now know that many other passerine families have evolved since the Corvidae first appeared.

Today, scientists believe that the corvid brain is an example of convergent evolution – the principle by which animals from different evolutionary lineages develop similar adaptations independently in response to a shared environmental challenge. Thus, for example, South America's armadillos (order Cingulata) and Africa's pangolins (order Pholidota) both have armoured bodies, digging claws and a long, sticky tongue as adaptations for breaking into anthills and eating ants, even though the two groups are entirely unrelated.

In the case of corvids and apes, both live in complex social groups and face similar challenges. Individuals must be able to recognise one another, track social positions, and remember and predict behaviour. What's more, they must keep updating all this information while adjusting their own behaviour accordingly. Intelligence, it seems, has evolved as an adaptation to the complexities of social living. This is, of course, the very principle that explains so much about our own species.

Many of the questions that surround corvid intelligence have no easy answers. Do crows think? Do Magpies have fun? Can Ravens feel guilty? It's easy to revert to anthropomorphism: to judge the actions of other animals by their resemblance to our own and thus risk attributing to them qualities that are not there. Nonetheless, the more scientists learn about corvids, the more remarkable they are proven to be. Studying corvids may thus not only teach us more about them, but also more about ourselves.

**Above:** What is this Rook thinking? Scientists may never know.

# Crows and People

People have enjoyed a love-hate relationship with corvids for as long as we have lived alongside them. In folklore and mythology, they have inspired both fear and reverence. In culture, they appear everywhere from horror story to nursery rhyme. Today, some landowners still regard many species as harmful pests; scientists, meanwhile, find they offer unique insights into animal behaviour. For the rest of us, corvids are among the few birds that we can watch wherever we find ourselves, and as such, they offer an enthralling avian accompaniment to our daily lives.

# Corvids in culture

Corvids have been as culturally significant as any birds throughout human history. They are enshrined in the mythologies of most major civilisations and societies, both in the eastern and western worlds, and are celebrated in art, religion and folklore to this day.

In most cultures, corvids are associated with death and mortality. This is probably explained by their taste for carrion, which in bygone ages extended to human corpses on gibbet or battlefield. Indeed, some ancient societies left out the bodies of the deceased to be picked clean by crows and Ravens – in the manner of Tibet's 'sky burials', where vultures traditionally perform the same role. It is thus perhaps unsurprising that many superstitions surrounding corvids depict the birds as evil or sinister. Many such beliefs also have a spiritual dimension, in which the birds are credited with the gifts of prophecy and insight, and are seen as emissaries between the spiritual and material worlds – mediators between life and death. In this respect, Ravens, described by the American writer and naturalist Peter Matthiessen (1927–2014) in Bernd Heinrich's *Ravens in Winter* (1989) as 'the great requiem bird of myth and legend', are especially revered.

**Opposite:** Hollywood director Alfred Hitchcock poses with Ravens in a publicity shot to promote his celebrated 1963 horror movie *The Birds*.

**Above:** Crows perch on a hangman's gibbet in a 19th-century wood engraving by Thomas Bewick (1753–1828).

**Above:** Ravens are often carved into totem poles in traditional Native American culture.

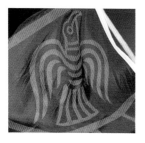

**Above:** A Raven represents the Norse god Odin in this Viking banner at Largs in Scotland.

Other associations with corvids entail cleverness and/or trickery, both of a positive and negative nature. This suggests that the intelligence of crows – their ability to use tools, mimic language and conceal objects – has piqued human curiosity since earliest times. Both Magpies and Jackdaws figure prominently in such beliefs.

## Myth and legend

Corvids feature prominently in mythologies around the world. The Raven is central to creation myths among the indigenous peoples of the northern Pacific, from the Tlingit and Inuit of north-west America to the Koryaks and Chukchis of north-east Russia. In the mythology of the Haida people of north-west Canada, it lived in the land of spirits, before humankind appeared, and created Earth by dropping a pebble in the sea.

In Europe, the Celtic peoples also saw corvids as manifestations of gods and rulers. Bendigeidfran, the Welsh giant king of legend, translates as 'Blessed Crow' or 'Blessed Raven', and the head of Brân the Blessed, as he became known, is now reputedly buried under the Tower of London, thus offering one explanation for the Ravens that are kept there to this day (see page 119). Morrígan, the Irish goddess of war and death, was also depicted as a Raven or crow. And the name of the Frankish King Guntram (c. AD 532–92) derives from Gontrand, which means 'War Raven'.

Our modern word 'raven' derives from the Old Norse *hrafn*, and nowhere in culture are Ravens more prominent than in Norse mythology. Viking chieftains went to war under the Raven banner, and the god Odin – revered in one form or another by the Germanic peoples since the Roman occupation – was generally accompanied by his Raven emissaries Huginn and Muninn, who brought him information from across the kingdom. Today, Ravens retain a more sinister cultural significance in Scandinavia: in Sweden as the ghosts of murdered men, and in Denmark as exorcised spirits.

Elsewhere, corvids feature in numerous creation myths. To the Aboriginal peoples of Australia, 'Crow' was an ancestral spirit, responsible for the theft of fire and the origin of death itself. In Hinduism, crows are traditionally viewed as bearers of information and omens: the Hindu deity Shani is often depicted riding on a giant black crow or raven, and a crow calling in front of a house in some regions is still thought to herald a special visitor. In Buddhism, Mahakala, the protector of dharma, or cosmic law and order, is represented in earthly form by a crow, and today the Raven is the national bird of the Buddhist kingdom of Bhutan.

Corvids were also an inspiration during classical times. An ancient Greek myth tells how the god Apollo, in a fit of pique, turned crows' feathers from white to black when a crow reported that his lover Coronis had been unfaithful. Another tells how Princess Arne of Siphnos was turned into a Jackdaw – a lover of shiny things – as punishment for her avarice, after being bribed by King Minos of Crete into betraying her island.

## Literature and the arts

Corvids have appeared in literature since early times. *The Crow and the Pitcher*, one of the fables of Aesop (c. 620– 564 BC), celebrates the intelligence of a crow that drops pebbles into a narrow-necked bottle until the water level is high enough to drink. Ravens repeatedly appear in the Bible, bringing Elijah food as he hides in a ravine (1 Kings 17:6) and being sent by Noah to look for land from the Ark (Genesis 8:7)

English literature is littered with corvids, from Geoffrey Chaucer (c. 1340s–1400) onwards. In *Barnaby Rudge* (1841), by Charles Dickens (1812–70), the title character has a pet Raven called Grip that mimics human speech. In 'The Raven' (1845), a poem by Dickens's contemporary Edgar Allan Poe (1809–49), the bird of the title is an ominous presence that dismays the narrator with its constant doom-laden repetition of 'nevermore'. In his 1970 collection of poems entitled *Crow*, Ted Hughes (1930–98) draws upon ancient myths to celebrate crows as a primal life force.

However, it is the plays of William Shakespeare (1564–1616) that give corvids their greatest literary airing. In *King Lear* (Act 4, Scene 6), Edgar talks of 'The crows and choughs that wing the midway air', while in *Othello* (Act 1, Scene 1), the treacherous Iago tells us: 'I will wear my heart upon my sleeve for daws to peck at'. And in *Macbeth*, the

**Below:** A Rook by French painter Édouard Manet (1832–83) features on the front cover of the original edition of 'The Raven' by Edgar Allan Poe.

play most saturated with evil and the supernatural, the bard really goes to town on the poetic power of corvids. 'The raven himself is hoarse | That croaks the fatal entrance of Duncan,' says Lady Macbeth as she steels herself before the murder of the king. And in Act 3, Scene 2, after the deed is done, Macbeth says to his wife, 'Light thickens, and the crow | Makes wing to th' rooky wood.'

## Popular culture

In contemporary popular culture, corvids are generally emblematic of the evil or sinister. On screen, the ragged black bird that attends bad people accompanies everyone from the evil queen in Disney's *Snow White and the Seven Dwarfs* (1937) to the antichrist in *Damien: Omen II* (1978). A Raven appears on the title credits for the US undertaker TV series *Six Feet Under*, and a formidable individual glares from the cover of the 1979 album *The Raven* by British punk band The Stranglers. Even when not purely evil, corvids are often used to evoke a world of historical myth or fantasy, from *Game of Thrones* to the *Harry Potter* series. The imagery invariably involves stark silhouettes, stricken tree stumps and perhaps a skull or two.

**Above:** A diabolical crow launches a vicious attack in the 1978 horror movie *Damien: Omen II*.

## Folklore

British folklore is littered with corvids. In rural life, Rooks have a particularly important place, their noisy rookeries providing an identity to villages and communities over generations. At least 170 places on the UK Ordnance Survey maps begin with 'Rook', including numerous Rook's Nests, Rook Hills and Rookery Farms. Today, the birds' high communal cawing is the soundtrack to rural life in countless dramas and documentaries, and it is telling that British colonists took Rooks to New Zealand, hoping to re-create the pastoral ambience from back home.

**Below:** The names of crows and other corvids are enshrined in numerous street names around the UK.

Folklore associated with Rooks includes the 'crow's wedding', the name given to the birds' display flights above their rookeries. The height at which the birds circle is held to predict the weather: the higher they go, the fairer it will be. Another myth that still persists is that of the 'parliament of Rooks'. The birds are said to gather in a circle on the ground to pass judgement upon one of their number who,

The importance of corvids in culture is illustrated by their influence on the English language. The following are just a few of the numerous idioms they have spawned.

*As the crow flies*: the most direct route between two locations (probably derived from the evening roosting flights of Rooks).
*Crow bait*: on its last legs – for example, describing an elderly or emaciated horse.
*Crow's feet*: wrinkles radiating from the corner of a person's eyes.
*Crow's nest*: lookout structure at the top of a ship's mast.
*Eat crow*: admit to a humiliating mistake or defeat.

*Popinjay*: a conceited, foppish or excessively talkative person.
*Raven-haired*: having hair that is black and lustrous, like a Raven's plumage.
*Rook*: to fool or dupe.
*Shoot the crow*: hurry away quickly, leaving obligations behind.
*Stone the crows*: exclamation of incredulity or annoyance (Australian slang).
*Up with the crows*: rising early (Australian slang).

guilty of some wrongdoing, sits in the middle to await the verdict. If found guilty by this avian court, the miscreant is pecked to death by the others. This brutal myth may have arisen from observing the habit of Rooks and other corvids of gathering around their dead companions.

The Chough has also inspired various odd beliefs, including that it has a propensity for starting fires – as celebrated in its scientific name *Pyrrhocorax* (literally 'fire raven'). This may derive from times when the bird was kept as a pet; perhaps it carried lighted candles around the house. Either way, Choughs have a special significance in Cornwall, where they were once common. Cornish myth holds that the legendary King Arthur did not die but was transformed into a Chough and, to this day, the bird remains emblazoned on the county's coat of arms.

No British corvid has generated more folklore than the Magpie. An ancient belief in the bird as an ill omen explains the widespread tradition of offering any lone Magpie a formal greeting – typically something like 'Good morning Mr Magpie; how are Mrs Magpie and all the little Magpies?' Other rituals traditionally required of those meeting a lone Magpie include standing and saluting. Today, schoolchildren still count Magpies with the classic ditty 'One for sorrow, two for joy, three for a girl, four for a boy, five for silver, six for gold, seven for a secret never to

**Below:** In this 1910 illustration from *Field Babies* by Cecil Aldin (1870–1935), a Magpie is depicted as typically mischievous.

be told'. There are many variations on this rhyme, which dates back to at least the 18th century. All suggest the same idea: that Magpies have prophetic powers and that we'd do well to keep on their good side. A belief in Magpies' propensity for stealing valuables (see below) also persists.

## An eye for the shiny?

The alleged attraction of Magpies and other corvids to jewellery and other shiny, valuable objects forms part of the folklore of most Western nations. In Gioachino Rossini's 1817 opera *La Gazza Ladra* (*The Thieving Magpie*), servant girl Ninetta is sentenced to death for stealing coins and silverware, only – spoiler alert – to be reprieved from the gallows when the items are found in the nest of a Magpie. The myth persists to this day and was even central to a 1985 national police information campaign against car theft, in which a Magpie's image featured as the warning logo.

Of course, Magpies have no idea how much we humans value coins and jewellery. However, they are highly inquisitive birds and will often investigate unusual objects they find. Such behaviour derives from their instinctive habit of caching food (see page 69), and those who have kept these birds as pets testify to their propensity for hiding small household items. However, studies have been unable to prove that Magpies have a particular appetite for bling. In an experiment at Exeter University, captive Magpies were offered an assortment of shiny and non-shiny objects but showed no preference for the former. 'There is absolutely no evidence that people have ever found anything silver or shiny in a magpie's nest,' concludes ecologist and Magpie expert Tim Birkhead, who studied the birds over a 10-year period.

The thieving myth probably derives from bygone days when people routinely kept Magpies as pets, and the birds were thus more likely to pick up items of value around the house. Indeed, Rossini based his opera on an 1815 Parisian melodrama, *La Pie Voleuse*

**Above:** A young Magpie clutches a sparkly trinket. But is this habit or just chance?

(also *The Thieving Magpie*), by Louis-Charles Caigniez and Théodore Baudouin d'Aubigny, which turns on just such an event. It seems likely that play and opera combined were responsible in large part for embedding this myth in contemporary culture.

There is no doubt, however, that the attention of a Magpie will sometimes fall on something shiny. Personal experience bears this out. Early one Easter Sunday morning, my father was baffled by the disappearance of all 30 foil-wrapped mini chocolate eggs that, just an hour earlier, he had hidden around the back garden for my six-year-old daughter to find when she got up. While searching in vain for the missing eggs, we noticed a Magpie watching us. Unable to believe that the bird could be the culprit ('*How* many, Dad?!'), we shooed it away and, when we thought it was out of sight, quickly hid two more eggs. As soon as we were back indoors, the bird reappeared and, within seconds, had located these eggs and carried them off before our eyes. Whether it subsequently became a chocoholic, we will never know.

# Ravens in the Tower

The last record of wild Ravens nesting in London was in Hyde Park in 1826. The species has always retained a pied-à-terre in the capital, however, courtesy of the ceremonial birds kept at the Tower of London, founded by William the Conqueror in 1078. Superstition has it that if the Ravens are lost from the Tower, the Crown will fall and Britain with it. Thus, to this day, a permanent collection of at least six individuals inhabits the ancient building and their wings are clipped to prevent them from flying away.

This superstition is said to date back to King Charles II (1630–85). When royal astronomer John Flamsteed complained that Ravens flying around the White Tower were obscuring the view from his telescope, the king reputedly first had the birds' wings clipped, and then in 1675 moved the Royal Observatory to Greenwich rather than lose them from the Tower. Some say that Ravens were brought to the Tower to dramatise executions, including that of Anne Boleyn in 1536 and Lady Jane Grey in 1554. Others claim that the superstition pre-dates this and derives from the ancient Welsh giant and king of the Britons Brân the Blessed, whose name means 'Raven' and whose head is said to have been buried beneath the Tower, facing defiantly towards France. However, some contemporary historians suspect all these stories to be flights of fancy concocted by the Victorians, noting that the earliest illustration of Ravens in the Tower hails from 1883.

Whatever the truth, the emblematic importance of these birds to the life of the nation remained strong enough for Winston Churchill to order the recruitment of six more Ravens after the Second World War, as only one (named Gripp) had survived the Blitz. Today, the Ravens are fed and cared for by the Ravenmaster of the Yeoman Warders (the Beefeaters, whose other traditional duties include protecting the Crown jewels). Each individual has a name and a colour ring and is officially enlisted as a soldier – thus subject to dismissal for 'unsatisfactory conduct', as happened to one miscreant that persistently attacked TV aerials. All have the flight feathers on one wing clipped every three weeks, allowing them to fly a little but not far enough to leave. The birds remain a major tourist attraction, and on 23 April (St George's Day) 2019, four chicks hatched to the mated pair Huginn and Muninn. These were the first Ravens to have hatched in London for nearly 200 years.

**Above:** Ravens in the Tower of London.

# Corvids and conservation

Today, UK corvids are faring pretty well. All eight breeding species are Green-listed, so are not of conservation concern, and several are among our commonest birds. Latest population estimates (see page 9) show that the Carrion Crow, Rook and Jackdaw all number more than a million breeding pairs, with Magpie, Hooded Crow and Jay in the hundreds of thousands. The Raven is less numerous, with around 7,000 breeding pairs, but this population is increasing. The Chough – the one rarity, with about 430 breeding pairs, including the Isle of Man – is also on the increase, hence its green status (see page 9).

Unlike many birds, corvids have largely benefited from humankind. The land we have cleared and the towns we have built have created new feeding opportunities and nest sites, allowing many species to thrive – and even to increase their numbers as development continues. However, this does not mean people have always got along with corvids. For centuries, we have persecuted these birds for the damage they are thought to cause.

## Corvids and the law

Like all UK birds, corvids – and their nests and eggs – are protected by law under the Wildlife and Countryside Act 1981. However, some species may be killed under the terms of a general licence from the Department of Environment, Food and Rural Affairs if they are deemed to threaten public health or cause severe damage to crops or livestock. The species to which this applies includes Carrion Crow, Rook, Jackdaw, Magpie and Jay. Hooded Crows and Ravens may also be killed under specific licences by application. All birds controlled under licence must be killed by humane methods, as stipulated. As well as shooting, control methods include the use of traps such as Larsen traps or ladder traps, in which corvids are lured by the presence of

**Above:** A trapped Magpie and its captive lure in a Larsen trap.

a captive bird and then humanely dispatched. Strict rules govern the use of such traps, including ensuring the welfare of the captive lure.

**Above:** A macabre reminder that
corvids are not always welcome
on farms.

The killing accelerated in the latter half of the 17th
century when the wider availability of guns provided
a deadlier alternative to scarecrows. With the advent
of Pheasant shooting during the Victorian era, corvids
acquired a new enemy in the form of the gamekeeper.
Persecution was relentless, and the birds' numbers
declined. By the start of the 20th century, Magpies and
Jays were both much less common than they are today
and Ravens (which had a bounty on their heads) had
disappeared from many regions, retreating to the country's
wildest corners.

Today, there is still hostility towards corvids among
some farming and gamekeeping communities. Large
numbers are legally killed every year (see box, opposite),
and the issue of attacks on lambs during the lambing
season (see page 62) remains contentious. This hostility
extends to some suburban communities, where recent
years have seen repeated calls for the culling of Magpies
to reduce their predation on songbirds (see page 61). In
some situations, conservationists have also had to resort
to legally culling a small number of Carrion and Hooded
Crows where they have been proven to reduce the
breeding success of rare birds – notably ground-nesting
species such as waders.

# Enjoying and learning from crows

Corvids may have benefited from people but they have also given plenty back. In a few cases, this involves tangible products. Jays, historically, were prized for their electric-blue wing feathers, used by milliners to decorate hats and by anglers as fly-fishing lures. Rooks were once a popular dish: the young birds, called 'branchers', were harvested from their nests just before they fledged – hence the nursery rhyme 'Sing a Song of Sixpence' describes 'four and twenty black birds baked in a pie'.

Most benefits we've derived from corvids, however, have been in the form of services rather than products. For example, while some farmers continue to guard against damage corvids may cause, many also recognise that Rooks and Jackdaws do a vital job by removing weeds and harmful insects, and turning over soil.

To scientists, corvids have been an invaluable resource in studies of animal behaviour. The social hierarchies of Jackdaws were central to the work of Konrad Lorenz (1903–89), known as the founding father of ethology – the study of animal behaviour. In more recent times, studies of species such as the California Scrub Jay and New Caledonian Crow have shed significant light on the

**Above:** Jay feathers were once prized as adornments for hats, brooches and fishing flies.

**Right:** Many people have formed close bonds with tame or hand-reared corvids.

**Left:** A Carrion Crow mixes easily with people in a city park.

structure of the avian brain and on the higher cognitive capacities of species other than humans, including memory, causal reasoning, tool use, self-awareness and empathy.

Among the many people who have kept corvids as pets are such luminaries as the poets Lord Byron (1788–1824) and John Clare (1793–1864), the American writer Truman Capote (1924–84) and the naturalist Gerald Durrell (1925–95). Those who have done so, typically by acquiring an abandoned or injured fledgling, testify to both the great rewards and serious challenges of living with these highly intelligent and responsive birds. Pet corvids respond to humans as individuals. They will learn commands, mimic speech, and cement their relationship with an owner by regular allogrooming and the presentation of gifts. They will also destroy crockery, make a terrible mess, hide treasured possessions and give a torrid time to cats and other household pets.

Of course, any corvid is better off in the wild. These are sociable birds that require interaction with their own kind. It is strongly recommended to leave young corvids well alone as their parents will be in the area. For further advice on looking after injured corvids, contact the RSPCA on 0300 1234 999 or the SPCA in Scotland on 03000 999 999.

# Watching corvids

There is no need to devote a lifetime to keeping or studying corvids to enjoy them. These birds are all around us, and we can easily watch them around our home – whether urban housing estate, leafy suburbia or rural village – or out in the surrounding countryside.

In town, look out for Carrion Crows – often very tame in parks, where they may scavenge alongside pigeons and gulls. Take time to observe their behaviour, and you'll appreciate from up close their social interactions, foraging skills and surprising vocal range. Magpies are also conspicuous in urban environments and, like crows, often strut about on rooftops. Listen for their rattling calls – they often betray a prowling cat – and watch for their gatherings on golf courses. Jackdaws in town tend to reveal themselves by their yapping call; look out for pairs around chimney pots, and larger, noisier gatherings when seeing off a Carrion Crow or Magpie. Castles, churches and other old buildings often host Jackdaw communities.

In the countryside, Rooks are often the most visible corvid – whether in flocks foraging in fields or gathering at their noisy treetop rookeries. They are often accompanied by Jackdaws. Watch how the two birds feed differently on the ground and separate in their mixed flocks in flight. Rookeries are great to observe in early spring, when the birds are busy displaying and building nests, but Rook-watching is also rewarding in early winter, when the movement of large flocks to their roosts is one of the more impressive British bird spectacles. Urban dwellers may notice how rural corvids are much harder to approach than their urban cousins, having learned to be wary of people. Personal experience suggests that a long camera lens breeds suspicion – perhaps because it resembles a shotgun.

Woodland is the best place to see Jays. These colourful corvids seldom perch in plain view, but listen for their screeching call and look out for the flash of colour as they fly away. In suburbia, any tree cover in quiet areas, including parks and cemeteries, can be good; if you're lucky, they may even visit your garden. Jays are easiest to

**Above:** Jackdaws are easily observed when they visit bird tables.

**Below:** A quiet urban cemetery is an ideal place to observe Jays.

see in autumn when making their lurching flights between woods as they gather and cache acorns, often overflying roads in the process.

At the coast, Jackdaws can be particularly tame at popular holiday locations, often foraging for scraps in car parks, picnic spots and seaside towns. Cliff paths allow you to watch their aerial prowess as they ride the breezes. Here, you may also find Ravens, typically a pair cruising the cliffs and betrayed by their call. Elsewhere, Ravens are best seen in upland areas in western and northern Britain, sometimes soaring very high and often doing aerial battle with crows or raptors. They are now increasing in number elsewhere, however, so stay alert for that wedge-shaped tail, deep *cronk* call and tumbling flight display.

To see our rarest corvid, the Chough, you'll need to visit one of its few haunts, namely the Welsh coast (especially Pembrokeshire and Anglesey), the Isle of Man, the Scottish island of Islay or Cornwall (from St Ives to Land's End). In good Chough country, these birds aren't hard to find. Walk the coastal paths, listen for their high *kyow* call and look for their acrobatics. One glimpse of that red bill, and you'll know instantly what you've seen.

**Below:** A Chough back at home on a Cornish clifftop.

## Choughs return to Cornwall

The year 1973 was a sad one for Cornwall, as it was then that the county's last remaining Chough disappeared. This emblematic bird had been in steep decline in Cornwall for years, and had not bred there since 1947. Ornithologists were delighted, therefore, when in 2001 five individuals turned up on The Lizard, in the county's far southwest, having crossed the Irish Sea from Ireland. In 2002, two of these birds paired up and bred. Over the following years they produced many youngsters, some of which have since raised young of their own. By June 2020, with Britain still in Covid-19 lockdown, 14 pairs of Choughs were breeding around the Cornish coast and, between them, had produced a total of 43 youngsters.

The return of the Choughs represents a conservation success story for the Cornish Chough Project, through which the RSPB, Natural England and the National Trust are working with local farmers and land managers to safeguard the new population. The project's work includes restoring habitats, protecting nest sites and promoting local awareness. Meanwhile, Operation Chough, established in 1987, is breeding Choughs in captivity and conducting ongoing research to build up a population of birds for potential reintroduction, through which it hopes to help broaden the wild gene pool. With occasional wandering individuals also arriving from Brittany and south Wales, scientists hope the Chough is now well on the way to re-establishing itself permanently in the county whose coat of arms still proudly bears its image.

# Glossary

**Allogrooming** Reciprocal grooming between two individuals of the same species – typically a mated pair, or members of a family or social group.
**Anthropogenic** Caused or produced by human activity. For example, global warming from carbon dioxide emissions is an anthropogenic phenomenon.
**Cavity nester** A bird that habitually nests in holes or crevices, typically in a tree trunk, cliffs or riverbank. Woodpeckers and tits are all cavity nesters.
**Commensalism** The biological relationship between two species in which only one benefits but the other is unharmed – unlike parasitism, where one species (the host) suffers.
**Endemic** Native to a particular place and naturally found only in that place.
**Fledging** The process through which baby birds develop the feathers and wing muscles required for flight and are able finally to leave the nest.
**Green-listed** UK conservation bodies list all British birds by conservation status: Red-listed birds are the most endangered; Amber-listed birds are also under threat; Green-listed birds are of least concern.
**Invertebrates** Insects, spiders and other small creatures, often known as 'bugs'. Invertebrate means

'without a backbone'; birds have backbones and are therefore vertebrates.
**Monogamous** Having only one mate at a time. Some birds are seasonally monogamous, taking a new mate each year; others, including most corvids, may form lifelong monogamous bonds.
**Palaearctic** The zoogeographical region comprising Europe and Asia north of the Himalayas, plus North Africa and the temperate part of the Arabian Peninsula. Europe lies within the Western Palaearctic, which is separated from the Eastern Palaearctic by Russia's Ural Mountains.
**Passerine** Any member of the Passeriformes order of birds, also known as perching birds. Roughly half the world's birds belong to this order, including the Corvidae (crow family).
**Subspecies** The geographical subdivision of a species, sometimes known as a 'race'. Subspecies differ by slight variations in size or appearance and each has a three-part name. For example, the Carrion Crow *Corvus corone* has two subspecies: the Western Carrion Crow *Corvus corone corone* of Europe, and the larger Eastern Carrion Crow *Corvus corone orientalis* of Asia. Both belong to the same species.
**Taxonomy** The science of classifying all life forms.

# Further Reading and Resources

Birkhead, T. 1998. *The Magpies: The Ecology and Behaviour of Black-billed and Yellow-billed Magpies.* Poyser, London. Highly readable scientific study of the Eurasian Magpie and its American cousin.
Cocker, M. 2008. *Crow Country: A Meditation on Birds, Landscape and Nature.* Vintage, London. Fascinating, beautifully written study of Rooks and rookeries around the author's Norfolk home, with reflections on the cultural importance of corvids.
Cocker, M. & Mabey, R. 2020. *Birds Britannica.* 2nd edn. Chatto and Windus, London. Beautifully illustrated account of the natural and cultural history of Britain's birdlife, with detailed accounts of all corvids.
Heinrich, B. 2007. *Mind of the Raven: Investigations and Adventures with Wolf-birds.* Ecco Press, New York. Fascinating study of Ravens, both captive and in the wild, by a leading expert.
Madge, S. 1999. *Crows and Jays: A Guide to the Crows, Jays and Magpies of the World.* Helm, London. Comprehensive guide to Corvidae worldwide, with maps and illustrations.
Marzluff, J.M. & Angell, T. 2007. *In the Company of Crows and Ravens.* Yale University Press, New Haven. Illuminating account of the cultural co-evolution of corvids and humans, co-written by a leading American scientist and a celebrated nature writer.
Savage, C. 2018. *Bird Brains: The Intelligence of Crows, Ravens, Magpies and Jays.* Greystone Books, Vancouver. Detailed look at the lives of the Corvidae from a celebrated nature writer.
Shute, J. 2018. *A Shadow Above: The Fall and Rise of the Raven.* Bloomsbury Wildlife, London. A fascinating

chronicle of the return of the Raven and the people who have made that comeback possible.
Woolfson, E. 2018. *Corvus: A Life with Birds.* Granta Books, London. Entertaining and thought-provoking account of raising an abandoned Rook and Magpie.

## Online resources

**Corvid Blog** *corvid-isle.co.uk.* Blog that provides an online forum for those interested in corvids.
**Find a Bird** *rspb.org.uk/birds-and-wildlife/wildlife-guides/bird-a-z/.* The RSPB's information section about UK birds, including corvids, with video and audio clips.
**For the Love of Crows** *facebook.com/groups/150923258692648.* Public Facebook group for people who love crows and all things corvid.
**Identifying Corvids – Crow, Chough, Jackdaw, Rook and Raven** *bto.org/develop-your-skills/bird-identification/videos/bto-bird-id-corvids.* Excellent British Trust for Ornithology video guide to identifying UK corvids.
**YouTube** *youtube.com.* Numerous video clips of corvids in action, including illuminating and entertaining amateur footage.

## Conservation organisations

**British Trust for Ornithology (BTO)**
*bto.org.* Research and monitoring organisation for Britain's birdlife. It also coordinates citizen science projects, including Garden Birdwatch.

**The Royal Society for the Protection of Birds (RSPB)**
*rspb.org.uk.* The RSPB is the UK's largest nature conservation charity and manages reserves around the country for birds and other wildlife, and their habitats.

**Wildlife Trusts**
*wildlifetrusts.org.* National conservation charity comprising 47 separate regional Wildlife Trusts across the UK. These offer information and advice on all aspects of British wildlife, and an extensive network of reserves.

# Acknowledgements

Many thanks to Julie Bailey and all at Bloomsbury Wildlife for bringing this book to fruition; especially to Jenny Campbell for her patience and editorial expertise; to copy-editor Susi Bailey for fine-tuning the text; to Lucy Beevor for diligent proofreading; and to designer Susan McIntyre for her excellent layouts. Thanks also to Julian Baker for the maps and illustrations, and Angie Hipkin for compiling the index.

Like any corvid enthusiast, I am indebted to the many naturalists whose studies of these much-maligned birds have shed light on their fascinating lives and helped foster a greater appreciation of what they bring to our world. On a personal note, I'd also like to thank my own family: my parents, who encouraged my love of nature from early days; and my wife Kathy and daughter Florence, with whom I've shared many memorable wildlife moments. And thanks, of course, to the birds themselves. This book was written during lockdown when *corvids* provided a welcome distraction from *covid* on my socially distanced walks around the local neighbourhood. 'So you're writing a book about covid,' soon became a familiar refrain.

# Image Credits

Bloomsbury Publishing would like to thank the following for providing photographs and permission to produce copyright material. While every effort has been made to trace and acknowledge all copyright holders, we would like to apologise for any errors or omissions and invite readers to inform us so that corrections can be made in any future editions of the book.

Key: t = top; l = left; r = right; c = centre; b = bottom; bl = bottom right; br = bottom right.

AL = Alamy; DT = David Tipling/birdphoto.co.uk; G = Getty Images; IS = iStock; JB = Julian Baker; MU = Mike Unwin; NPL = Nature Picture Library; RS = RSPB Images; SH = Shutterstock.

**Front cover** t Ben Andrew/RSPB Images, b BIOSPHOTO/AL; **spine** Mark Richardson Imaging; **back cover** t Kneonlight/IS, b Monika Surzin/SH; **1** birdsonline/G; **3** Erni/SH; **4** Tom Meaker/SH; **6** Ian Hay/RS; **7** imageBROKER/AL; **8** Education Images/Contributor/G; **10** t MU, b JB; **12** t kaczor58/SH, c Education Images/Contributor/G, b JB; **13** M & J Bloomfield/AL; **14** t DT, b JB; **15** Nick Upton/NPL; **17** t MU, b JB; **18** MU; **19** Nature Photographers Ltd/AL; **20** t DT, b JB; **21** Markus Varesvuo/NPL; **23** t Erni/SH, b JB; **24** David J Slater/RS; **25** MU; **26** JB; **27** Minden Pictures/AL; **28** Menno Schaefer/SH; **29** JB; **30** Andyworks/G; **31** Erni/SH; **32** MikhailSh/SH; **34** l MU, r Butterfly Hunter/SH; **36** Javi Carvajal/AL; **37** t Paul Souders/AL, b ZSSD/NPL; **38** l MU, r MU; **39** l Nick Upton/NPL, r Svitlana Tkach/SH; **40** t Steve Taylor ARPS/AL, b Wirestock Images/SS; **41** MU; **42** t Martin Lindsay/AL, b Don Mammoser/SH; **43** l MU, r MU; **44** FLPA/AL; **45** Wikipedia Commons; **46** DT; **47** Emile E Wendling/SH; **48** l Tony Quinn/EyeEm/G, r MU; **49** t xpixel/SH, b Bennekom/SH; **50** MU; **51** t Radovan Zierik/SH, b Natalia Paklina/SH; **52** Marcin Perkowski/SH; **53** MU; **54** Markus Varesvuo/NPL; **55** Fuller Photography/SH; **56** undefined undefined/G; **57** Pat Bennett/AL; **58** l Chris Rabe/AL, r Erni/SH; **59** t Richard Becker/AL, b Ian Wade Photography/G; **60** t Arterra/Contributor/G, b Oliver Smart/AL; **61** BRIAN BEVAN/AL; **62** Chris Robbins/AL; **63** Giedriius/SH; **64** JakubD/SH; **65** Mike Potts/NPL; **66** Vishnevskiy Vasily/SH; **67** t Juniors Bildarchiv GmbH/AL, b MU; **68** Christian Paoli/G; **69** Sandra Standbridge/SH; **70** Jana Scigelova/AL; **71** Andyworks/G; **72** Richard Bedford/RS; **73** MU; **74** MU; **75** LISA MOORE/AL; **76** l DT, r Paul Cumberland/AL; **77** Leopardinatree/IS; **78** t MU, b Donata Ivanova/IS; **79** MU; **80** PjrNature/AL; **81** DT; **82** blickwinkel/AL; **83** keith Burdett/AL; **84** Dave Bevan/NPL; **86** Jim Hallett/NPL; **87** DT; **88** birdpix/AL; **89** l Dgwildlife/IS, r Eremeychuk Leonid/AL; **90** t MikeLane45/G, bl Akabei/G, br David Hosking/AL; **91** l MU, r AnnaPH/SH; **92** Sergii Petruk/AL; **93** Richard Clarkson/AL; **94** imageBROKER/AL; **95** t MU, b MU; **96** BIOSPHOTO/AL; **97** Karel Bartik/SH; **98** t BRIAN BEVAN/AL, b MU; **99** t Lumpan/IS, b Piotr Velixar/SH; **100** Chris Gomersall/AL; **102** Nature Picture Library/AL; **103** Auscape International Pty Ltd/AL; **104** t Tom Mason/RS, b donikz/SH; **105** robin chittenden/AL; **106** DT; **107** Alex Puddephatt/SH; **108** t Andrew Darrington/AL, b Sourabh Bharti/SH; **109** Agami Photo Agency/SH; **110** JB; **111** DT; **112** ScreenProd/Photononstop/AL; **114** t Granger Historical Picture Archive/AL, c Nnehring/G, b MediaWorldImages/AL; **115** Artokoloro/AL; **116** t AA Film Archive/AL, b Coombs Images/AL; **117** Chronicle/AL; **118** fotostok_pdv/IS; **119** Ernie Janes/SH; **120** Joe Blossom/AL; **121** andrew payne/AL; **122** t MU, b Alex Linch/AL; **123** Nick Upton/2020VISION/NPL; **124** t Tom Askaroff/SH, b MU; **125** Richard Bedford/RS.

# Index